FUTURE 1

English for Work, Life, and Academic Success

Second Edition

Author
Margot Gramer

Series Consultants
**Sarah Lynn
Ronna Magy
Federico Salas-Isnardi**

 Pearson

Future 1 Workbook
English for Work, Life, and Academic Success
Copyright © 2019 by Pearson Education, Inc.

Pearson Education, 221 River Street, Hoboken, NJ 07030 USA

Staff credits: The people who made up the **Future 1 Workbook** team, representing content development, design, manufacturing, marketing, multimedia, project management, publishing, rights management, and testing, are Pietro Alongi, Jennifer Castro, Dave Dickey, Gina DiLillo, Warren Fischbach, Pamela Fishman, Gosia Jaros-White, Joanna Konieczna, Michael Mone, Mary Rich, Katarzyna Starzyńska-Kościuszko, Claire Van Poperin, Joseph Vella, Gabby Wu.

Text composition: Dataflow International
Cover design: EMC Design Ltd
Audio: CityVox

ISBN-13: 978-0-13-454759-6
ISBN-10: 0-13-454759-4

Printed in the United States of America

13 2022

CONTENTS

TO THE TEACHER

The *Future 1 Workbook* has 12-page units to complement what students have learned in the Student Book. Each Workbook unit follows the lesson order of the Student Book and provides supplemental practice in vocabulary, listening and speaking, grammar, reading, writing, soft skills, and workplace, life, and community skills. Students can complete the exercises outside the classroom as homework or during class to extend instruction.

The Workbook audio provides practice with conversations, grammar, and workplace, life, and community skills competencies. In addition, the audio includes the readings from the Workbook so students can become more fluent readers.

UNIT STRUCTURE

Vocabulary

Practice focuses on the vocabulary presented on the first spread of the unit. Typical activities are word and sentence completion, labeling, and categorizing. Some lessons include sentence writing to reinforce the lesson's vocabulary, and some lessons include personalized exercises.

Grammar and Listening

Grammar is the main focus, with listening practiced as well. Grammar is practiced in contextualized exercises that include sentence completion, sentence writing, sentence scrambles, matching, and multiple choice. Listening activities include listening comprehension, listening dictation, and listening to check answers. Some lessons include vocabulary exercises to reinforce the new vocabulary taught in the lesson. Some lessons include personalized activities.

Workplace, Life, and Community Skills

In the second edition, the Life Skills lesson has been revised to focus on workplace, life, and community skills and to develop the real-life language and civic literacy skills required today. Lessons integrate and contextualize workplace content. In addition, every lesson includes practice with digital skills on a mobile device.

Writing

In the second edition, a cumulative writing lesson has been added to every unit. This new lesson requires students to synthesize and apply their learning in a written outcome. Through a highly scaffolded approach, students begin by analyzing writing models before planning and finally producing written work of their own.

Reading

All reading lessons have new, information-rich texts and a revised pedagogical approach in line with the CCR and ELP standards and the NRS descriptors. These informational texts are level appropriate, use high-frequency vocabulary, and focus on interpretation of graphic information. The readings build students' knowledge and develop their higher-order reading skills by teaching citation of evidence, summarizing, and interpretation of complex information from a variety of text formats.

Soft Skills at Work

Future has further enhanced its development of workplace skills by adding a Soft Skills at Work lesson to each unit. Soft skills are the critical interpersonal communication skills needed to succeed in any workplace. Students begin each lesson by discussing a common challenge in the workplace. Then, while applying the lesson-focused soft skill, they work to find socially appropriate solutions to the problem.

ADDITIONAL RESOURCES

At the back of the Workbook, you will find:
- Audio Script
- Answer Key

ORIENTATION

The Workbook, like the Student Book, includes an orientation for students. Before the students use the Workbook for the first time, direct them to To the Student on the next page. Go through the questions and tips with the students and answer any questions they may have so they can get the most out of using the Workbook.

WL_09.21.2022_1157

Lesson 3: Workplace, Life, and Community Skills

A ▶ Listen. Complete the names.

1. <u>C a s a n d r a</u>

2. ___ ___ ___ ___ ___ ___

3. ___ ___ ___ ___ ___ ___

4. ___ ___ ___ ___ ___ ___

5. ___ ___ ___ ___ ___

6. ___ ___ ___ ___ ___ ___

B ▶ Listen. Complete the forms.

1.

❏ Mr.   ❏ Mrs.

❏ Ms.   ❏ Miss

First name: ___<u>Allie</u>___

Last name: _____

2.

❏ Mr.   ❏ Mrs.

❏ Ms.   ❏ Miss

First name: _____

Last name: _____

3.

❏ Mr.   ❏ Mrs.

❏ Ms.   ❏ Miss

First name: _____

Last name: _____

Lesson 1: Vocabulary

A Complete the names of the countries.

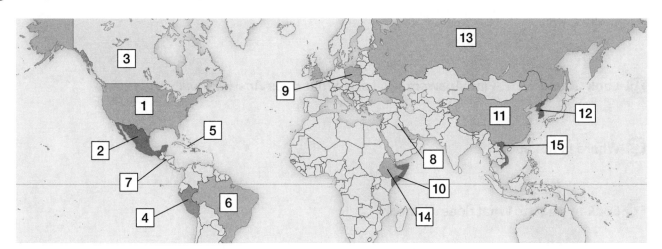

1. _T_ _h_ e U _n_ i _t_ ed Sta _t_ es

2. Me __ i __ __

3. Ca __ a __ a

4. Pe __ u

5. Cu __ a

6. Bra __ il

7. E __ Sa __ va __ or

8. I __ aq

9. __ o __ and

10. So __ alia

11. Chi __ a

12. Sou __ __ Ko __ ea

13. __ ussi __

14. E __ __ io __ ia

15. __ ie __ na __

B Write the name of a country in the region.
Use a country from Exercise A.

1. ___The United States___ is in North America.

2. _____ is in Asia.

3. _____ is in Europe.

4. _____ is in the Middle East.

5. _____ is in South America.

6. _____ is in Central America.

7. _____ is in Africa.

Lesson 2: Listening

A Look at the IDs. Write sentences.

1.
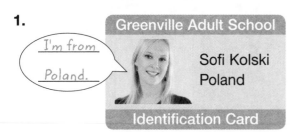
I'm from Poland.
Greenville Adult School
Sofi Kolski
Poland
Identification Card

2.

Greenville Adult School
Debra Leon
El Salvador
Identification Card

3.

Greenville Adult School
Min Dong
Vietnam
Identification Card

4.
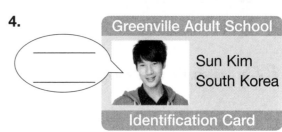
Greenville Adult School
Sun Kim
South Korea
Identification Card

B Look at the IDs in Exercise A. Complete the sentences.

1. Sofi Kolski _____*is from Poland*_____.

2. Debra Leon _____.

3. Min Dong _____.

4. Sun Kim _____.

C Put the conversation in the correct order. Write the correct numbers.

___ Nice to meet you, too.

___ Hi, Marta. I'm Celia.

___ Nice to meet you, Celia.

___ Where are you from?

___ I'm from Brazil. What about you?

_1_ Hi, I'm Marta.

___ I'm from Peru.

D ▶ Listen. Check your answers to Exercise C.

LEARN ABOUT YOUR BOOK

(A) **Look in the back of your book. Find each section. Write the page number.**

Audio Script ___   Answer Key ___

(B) **Look at page 157. Find *Answers will vary*. What does *Answers will vary* mean?**

(C) **Where is the audio?**

(D) **Look at page 5. What does ▶ mean?**

TIPS FOR USING THE AUDIO

Read the tips for using the audio.

- For all exercises, listen to each track many times.
- For dictation exercises, use the pause button so you can have more time to write.
- After you finish the unit, play the audio again and read the audio script in the back of the book at the same time.
- Also, for more listening practice, listen to the conversations and readings when you are in the car or on the bus.

WRITING TIPS

Read the writing tips.

- Start sentences with a capital letter.
- End statements with a period (.).
- End questions with a question mark (?).

For example:

My name is Jack.

What's your name?

C Look at the names. Put them in alphabetical order.

Most Common First Names for Female Babies in the U.S.

1.	Emma	1.	_Amelia_
2.	Olivia	2.	_____
3.	Ava	3.	_____
4.	Isabella	4.	_____
5.	Sophia	5.	_____
6.	Mia	6.	_____
7.	Charlotte	7.	_____
8.	~~Amelia~~	8.	_____

Source: Social Security Administration

D Look at the photos. Check the correct title.

1. ❑ Miss Jones
   ❑ Mrs. Jones

2. ❑ Mr. Kaz
   ❑ Ms. Kaz

3. ❑ Miss Cabo
   ❑ Mr. Cabo

4. ❑ Mr. Lin
   ❑ Mrs. Lin

Lessons 4 & 5: Listening and Grammar

A Complete the sentences. Use *am* or *is*.

1. I ___am___ from Cuba. I _____ in Level 2.

2. Sonya _____ from Russia. She _____ in Level 1.

3. Jonas _____ from Poland. He _____ a student.

B Rewrite the sentences. Replace the underlined words with *He* or *She*.

1. <u>Carla</u> is from Peru.

   She is from Peru.

2. <u>Mr. Kaz</u> is from Iraq.

   _____

3. <u>Mark</u> is from the United States.

   _____

4. <u>Jin</u> is from South Korea.

   _____

C Complete the conversations. Use pronouns and contractions.

1. **A:** Where's Ms. Johnson from?

   B: ___She's___ from Canada.

2. **A:** Where's Mrs. Nu from?

   B: _____ from Vietnam.

3. **A:** Where's Mr. Nowak from?

   B: _____ from Poland.

4. **A:** Where's Mr. Marmo from?

   B: _____ from Brazil.

D Rewrite the sentences in the negative. Then write another sentence. Use pronouns and contractions.

1. Katya is in Level 2. (Level 1)   *Katya is not in Level 2. She's in Level 1.*

2. Mani is from El Salvador. (Mexico)   _____

3. Mr. Fani is the teacher. (a student)   _____

4. I am in Level 3. (Level 1)   _____

E Look at the list. Correct the sentences.

Name	Country of Origin	Class
Ms. Cabral	Brazil	Level 3
Mr. Duval	Syria	Level 1
Mrs. Gao	China	Level 1
Mr. Medina	Mexico	Level 2
Mr. Molev	Russia	Level 3
Ms. Park	South Korea	Level 2

1. Ms. Cabral is from China.   *Ms. Cabral is not from China. She's from Brazil.*

2. Mr. Duval is in Level 2.   _____

3. Mrs. Gao is from Vietnam.   _____

4. Mr. Medina is from Brazil.   _____

5. Mr. Molev is in Level 2.   _____

6. Ms. Park is in Level 3.   _____

Lesson 6: Reading

Ⓐ DEVELOP YOUR ACADEMIC SKILLS. Read the Academic Skill. Complete the sentences.

1. Underline the title of the reading.

2. The topic will be _____
   a. the reasons immigrants come to the U.S.
   b. when immigrants come to the U.S.
   c. where immigrants are in the U.S.

> **Academic Skill: Use the title.**
> Before you read an article, look at the title of the article. The title can help you understand the article. It often identifies the topic.

Ⓑ ▶ Listen and read.

WHERE IMMIGRANTS LIVE IN THE U.S.

Immigrants live in many different regions of the United States. They often choose regions close to where they came from. Many immigrants live in California. California is close to Asia.
5 Many immigrants from countries like South Korea and China come to live in California. California also borders Mexico. Many immigrants from Mexico and countries in Central America come to California to live.
10 Texas is another state on the border of Mexico. Many immigrants come to Texas to live because it is close to their country.

Another reason that immigrants live in certain regions is because of people who already live there. They may have family members who live in states, such as
15 Texas or Florida, or even New York.

A third reason why immigrants might live in certain states is the weather. States like California, Texas, and Florida have warm weather. Immigrants from countries that are warm may prefer these states.

Finally, immigrants go places where there are jobs. Many states like California and Florida have farms. They need many workers. Immigrants go there to find work.

California 10.7 million
Texas 4.7 million
New York 4.5 million
Florida 4.2 million
New Jersey 2 million

Ⓒ CITE EVIDENCE. Complete the sentences. Where is the information? Write the line number.

Lines

1. Many immigrants from _____ live in Texas.
   a. South Korea   b. China   c. Mexico   _____

2. Immigrants live in states where they have _____.
   a. good schools   b. family   c. cheap places to live   _____

Ⓓ INTERPRET. Look at the map. Complete the sentences.

1. The state with the largest number of immigrants is _____.
   a. New York   b. Texas   c. California

2. Three states have a little more than 4 million immigrants. These are New York, _____.
   a. Texas, and New Jersey   b. Texas, and Florida   c. California, and Texas

Lessons 7 & 8: Listening and Grammar

A Complete the sentences. Use *is* or *are*. Then rewrite the sentences with contractions.

1. They ___are___ in Level 2.   _They're in Level 2._____

2. We _____ students.   _____

3. You _____ a student.   _____

4. Lev and I _____ from Russia.   _____

5. Marta and Han _____ in Level 3.   _____

6. It _____ interesting.   _____

B Unscramble the words to form sentences.

1. _We are from El Salvador._____
   (are / we / El Salvador / from)

2. _____
   (we / Level 2 / in / are)

3. _____
   (Brazil / Tomas and Celia / from / are)

4. _____
   (are / a / you / student)

5. _____
   (Tania and I / today / absent / are)

C Match the questions with the answers.

1. Hi, what class are you in? __d__   **a.** She's helpful.

2. How's the class? ____   **b.** They're great.

3. What about the students? ____   **c.** It's interesting.

4. How's the teacher? ____   ~~**d.**~~ We're in Level 3.

D Rewrite the sentences in the negative. Use contractions.

1. They're in Level 4.   _They're not in Level 4._

2. We're from Somalia.   _____

3. My English class is hard.   _____

4. Mr. and Mrs. Kim are from China. _____

5. Celia and I are students.   _____

6. Calvin and Ricardo are from El Salvador. _____

7. Diego and Armando are students. _____

8. This book is interesting.   _____

E ▶ Listen to the conversation. Write the missing words.

Rob: Who's that?

Ana: That's ___the teacher___.

Sue: That's _____ the teacher.

Ana: You're right. That's Mila.

Rob: Where's _____ from?

Ana: _____ from Russia. _____ in Level 1.

Rob: Who's that?

Ana: That's Juan.

Sue: That's _____ Juan.

Ana: You're right. That's Mr. Jones.

Rob: Where's _____ from?

Ana: _____ from the United States. _____ the teacher.

_____ great.

Lesson 9: Grammar

A Rewrite the sentences. Use *isn't* or *aren't*.

1. She's not in my class.　　　　　<u>She isn't in my class.</u>

2. Bob and Al are not absent.　　　　<u>　　　　　　　　　　　　　</u>

3. The teacher is not interesting.　　<u>　　　　　　　　　　　　　</u>

4. The students are not friendly.　　<u>　　　　　　　　　　　　　</u>

5. Level 2 is not hard.　　　　　　<u>　　　　　　　　　　　　　</u>

B Look at the pictures. Write new sentences. Use *isn't* or *aren't*. Write new sentences.

$$(x-1)^2 = (4\sqrt{x-4})^2$$
$$x^2 - 2x + 1 = 16(x-4)$$
$$x^2 - 2x + 1 = 16x - 64$$
$$x^2 - 18x + 65 = 0$$
$$(x-13)(x-5) = 0 \longrightarrow x = 13, x = 5$$

1. It's easy.

<u>It isn't easy. It's hard.</u>

2. She's from India.

<u>　　　　　　　　　　　　　</u>

3. He's in Level 2.

<u>　　　　　　　　　　　　　</u>

4. They're from Vietnam.

<u>　　　　　　　　　　　　　</u>

5. They're from China.

<u>　　　　　　　　　　　　　</u>

6. David is in school.

<u>　　　　　　　　　　　　　</u>

Lesson 10: Writing

A Read the Writing Skill. Then circle the capital letters for people and places.

1. My friend Suni is from India.

2. India is a country in Asia.

3. She's in Houston, Texas, now.

4. Suni is in the Greenville Adult School.

5. Ms. Brown is the teacher.

> **Writing Skill : Use capital letters**
>
> Names of people and places begin with a capital letter.
> For example:
>
> Carlos Gomez is from El Salvador.

B Look at the sentences in Exercise A again. Answer the question.

First word	Surname	Last word	First name

Where else do you use capital letters in a sentence?

_____

C Look at the picture. Complete the paragraph.

Greenville Adult School

Identification Card

My name ___is___ Min. I _____ from Hanoi, Vietnam. Vietnam _____ in Asia. It _____ a big country. It's small. Now I'm in San Francisco, California. _____ in school now. My teacher _____ Mr. Cooper. He _____ friendly. The students _____ also friendly. I _____ happy here.

D Read the text. Correct three errors with capital letters.

Ms. hale is my teacher. She's very interesting and friendly. She's from the united States. The students in my class are from India, china, and Mexico.

Lesson 11: Soft Skills at Work

A BE FRIENDLY. How can you be friendly at work? Check (✓) the correct answers.

❑ **a.** say hello

❑ **b.** smile at co-workers

❑ **c.** say nothing to co-workers

❑ **d.** call co-workers by their first name

Aki works at a store. She is a sales assistant.

B Aki meets a new co-worker at work. Cross out the incorrect words. Then circle *True* or *False*.

1. Aki: Hi, you're new, right?

Sam: Hi. Yes, I **is / am**. I'm sorry. What's **you / your** name?

Aki: I'm Aki. And **what's / how's** your name?

Sam: I'm Sam. Nice to **meet / see** you, Aki.

Aki: Nice to meet you **again / too**, Sam.

2. Sam is friendly to Aki.   True   False

C Aki meets another new co-worker at work. Cross out the incorrect words. Then circle *True* or *False*.

1. Aki: Hi, I'm Aki.

Ana: Hi.

Aki: **Nice / new** to meet you.

Ana: Yes.

Aki: **What's / Is** your name?

Ana: Ana.

2. Ana is friendly to Aki.   True   False

D JOB AWARENESS. Aki is a sales assistant in a store. She works with different people. She helps customers. Choose the correct answers.

1. Sales assistants talk to customers.   True   False

2. It is important to be friendly to customers.   True   False

Lesson 1: Vocabulary

A Complete the names of the jobs.

1. sa __l__ es assi __s__ __t__ a __n__ __t__
2. lan ___ sca ___ er
3. ___ omema ___ e ___
4. e ___ ectr ___ cia ___
5. dri ___ er

6. nur ___ e
7. chil ___ - ___ are ___ or ___ e ___
8. docto ___
9. ma ___ a ___ er

B Look at the pictures. Write the jobs. Use the words in Exercise A.

1. _____sales assistant_____

2. _____

3. _____

4. _____

5. _____

6. _____

7. _____

8. _____

9. _____

C Look at the picture. Write the jobs of the people. Use the words in the box.

cashier   cook   ~~doctor~~   server

1. _____ *doctor* _____

2. _____

3. _____

4. _____

D Look at the picture. Write the jobs of the people. Use the words in the box.

~~accountant~~   electrician   office assistant   painter

1. _____ *accountant* _____

2. _____

3. _____

4. _____

Lessons 2 & 3: Listening and Grammar

A Complete the sentences. Use *a* or *an*.

1. Kim is __a__ cashier.

2. Yuli is _____ custodian.

3. Mario is _____ painter.

4. Martin is _____ server.

5. Alex is _____ cook.

6. Eva is _____ office assistant.

B Combine the sentences.

1. Paul is a doctor. Rafael is a doctor.   *Paul and Rafael are doctors.* _____

2. Carla is a server. Luke is a server.   _____

3. Marco is a nurse. Tania is a nurse.   _____

4. Liam is a landscaper. Sal is a landscaper.   _____

5. Mia is an accountant. Luz is an accountant.   _____

6. Kim is a cashier. Mike is a cashier.   _____

C Complete the conversation. Use the sentences in the box.

Mike: Sonia, this is Marie. Marie, this is Sonia.

Sonia: Hi, Marie. It's nice to meet you.

Sue: _Nice to meet you, too, Sonia._ _____

Sonia: So, Marie, what do you do?

Marie: _____

Sonia: I'm an office assistant, too.

Marie: _____

> I'm an office assistant. What about you?
> ~~Nice to meet you, too, Sonia.~~
> Oh, that's interesting.

D ▶ Listen. Check your answers to Exercise C.

Lesson 4: Workplace, Life, and Community Skills

A ▶ Listen. Write the numbers.

0 1 2 ~~3~~ 4 5 6 7 8 9

1. _3_   **2.** ___   **3.** ___   **4.** ___   **5.** ___

6. ___   **7.** ___   **8.** ___   **9.** ___   **10.** ___

B Write the numbers in Exercise A in words.

1. _three_   **2.** _____   **3.** _____   **4.** _____   **5.** _____

6. _____   **7.** _____   **8.** _____   **9.** _____   **10.** _____

C ▶ Listen. Write the letter of the phone number you hear.

a.

302-555-7981

b.

903-555-8416

c.

302-555-6092

d.

903-555-3460

e.

302-555-8132

1. _d_   **2.** ___   **3.** ___   **4.** ___   **5.** ___

D Write the phone numbers and email addresses.

1. (two-one-two) five-five-five-three-four-eight-zero _____(212)555-3480_____

2. (seven-one-eight) five-five-five-nine-three-two-two _____

3. (smith-five-five-five@hmail.com) _____

4. (nine-one-four) five-five-five-four-four-three-eight _____

5. (mike-three-six-eight@hmail.com) _____

E ▶ Listen. Complete the phone numbers.

Places of Interest in Mountainville

The Blue Moon Restaurant . . . .(473) 555-3 <u>4</u> 4 <u>2</u>

Kay's Clothes Store . . . . (473) 555-8 __ __6

Mountainville Hospital . . . .(473) 555-__8__0

The Peamont Child-Care Center . . . . (473) 555-__7__8

Shelburn Office Supplies . . . .(473) 555-9 __ __7

F Find three contacts in your phone. Write their email address.
Write each phone number using numbers and words.

Contact name	Email	Phone number (numbers)	Phone number (words)
Carla	Carla1999@newmail.edu	(213) 555-1357	Two-one-three-five-five-five one-three-five-seven

Lessons 5 & 6: Listening and Grammar

A Complete the conversations. Use contractions when possible.

1. A: _Are_ you a teacher? **B:** Yes, I _am_.

2. A: _____ he a painter? **B:** No, he _____.

3. A: _____ your job hard? **B:** No, it _____.

4. A: _____ they servers? **B:** No, they _____.

5. A: _____ you a homemaker? **B:** No, I _____.

B Look at the pictures. Complete the conversations.

1. **A:** _Is Rob an electrician?_
   (Rob / electrician)

   B: _Yes, he is._

2. **A:** _____
   (Sara and Ann / cashiers)

   B: _____

3. **A:** _____
   (Mr. Ruiz / landscaper)

   B: _____

4. **A:** _____
   (Carl and Miguel / cooks)

   B: _____

5. **A:** _____
   (Jason / accountant)

   B: _____

6. **A:** _____
   (Bianca / doctor)

   B: _____

C ▶ Listen to the conversations. Write the correct occupation for each person.

1. _____cook_____
   Calvin

2. _____
   Ms. Torres

3. _____
   Hong-Yi

4. _____
   Kristina

5. _____
   Daniel

6. _____
   Elena

7. _____
   Rodrigo

8. _____
   Kim

9. _____
   Robert

D Look at Exercise C. Complete the conversations. Use the names in the parentheses.

1. **A:** That's Calvin. He's a cook.

   B: (Kristina) _Is Kristina a cook_, too?

   A: _No, she isn't. She's an accountant._

2. **A:** That's Daniel. He's an office assistant.

   B: (Ms. Torres) _____, too?

   A: _____

3. **A:** That's Hong-Yi. He's an electrician.

   B: (Calvin) _____, too?

   A: _____

4. **A:** That's Daniel. He's an office assistant.

   B: (Elena and Kristina) _____, too?

   A: _____

Lesson 7: Reading

A ▶ Listen and read.

GROWING HEALTHCARE JOBS

Many of the new jobs for the future will be in healthcare support. Two of these jobs are home health <u>aides</u> and personal care aides.

An aide is someone who helps people. Home health aides and personal care aides help people who are sick. They go to people's homes to help them. They help them get dressed and eat.

5 They can help people in different ways. They have different training. Home health aides have more training than personal care aides. Sometimes, they are CNAs (certified nursing assistants). That is why they can give people <u>medicine</u>. Personal care aides need a high school education. Personal care aides cannot give people medicine.

Home health aides make about $21,000 a year. Personal care aides make about $20,000 a year.

Employment projections data for home health aides and personal care aides, 2016-26

Occupational Title	Employment		Change, 2016-26	
	2016	2026	Numeric	Percent
Home health aides and personal care aides	2,927,600	4,136,400	1,208,800	41%
Home health aides	911,500	1,342,700	431,200	47%
Personal care aides	2,016,100	2,793,800	777,600	39%

Source: U.S. Bureau of Labor Statistics, Employment Projections Program

B DEVELOP YOUR ACADEMIC SKILLS. Read the Academic Skill. Look at the underlined words in the text. Match the word and its definition.

1. aide _____   **a.** something to help sick people get better

2. medicine _____   **b.** someone who helps people

> **Academic Skill: Learn new vocabulary**
> When you read words you don't know, write them down. You can write the words on cards or in your notebook. You can find the meaning in a dictionary.

C CITE EVIDENCE. Complete the sentences. Where is the information? Write the line number.

Lines

1. A lot of new jobs in the future will be in _____ support.
   a. technology   **b.** education   **c.** healthcare   _____

2. Personal care aides help sick people _____.
   a. in their home   **b.** in a hospital   **c.** in an office   _____

3. Home health aides make _____ personal care aides.
   a. less money than   **b.** more money than   **c.** as much money as   _____

D INTERPRET. Look at the chart. Complete the sentences.

1. There were more than _____ home health aides employed in 2016.
   a. 900,000   **b.** 1,000,000   **c.** 2,000,000

2. The number of personal care aides will increase by nearly _____ by 2026.
   a. 30%   **b.** 40%   **c.** 50%

Lessons 8 & 9: Listening and Grammar

A Complete the sentences. Use *work* or *works*. Then match the jobs with the places.

1. I __work__ at a school.   _c_   **a.** stock clerk

2. They _____ at a construction site.   ___   **b.** an assembly-line worker

3. Joe _____ at a factory.   ___   ~~**c.**~~ a teacher

4. Grace and Lucy _____ at a store.   ___   **d.** a caregiver

5. He _____ at a nursing home.   ___   **e.** carpenter

B Complete the sentences. Use *work* or *works*.

1. I ___work___ at a restaurant.   2. They _____ in Los Angeles.

3. He _____ at a school.   4. Ms. Bento _____ at an office.

5. We _____ in New York.   6. Dr. Yu _____ at a hospital.

C ▶ Listen. Match the sentences with the pictures.

1. ___

2. ___

3. _a_

4. ___

D Complete the sentences. Use the correct form of the verbs in parentheses.

1. My husband and I _____*are*_____ from Cuba. We _____ in Miami. My husband
         (be)   (live)

_____ at a hospital. I _____ at a bank.
    (work)   (work)

2. Carlos _____ a caregiver. He _____ at a nursing home. He _____ in Dallas.
              (be)   (work)   (live)

3. Martin and Thomas _____ in San Diego. They _____ accountants. They
                              (live)   (be)

_____ at an accounting office.
    (work)

E Complete the conversation. Use the sentences in the box.

Are you a student here?	~~Hi, I'm Edna.~~
I work in a nursing home.	I'm a nurse.
It's nice to meet you.	Really? That's interesting.

Edna: _Hi, I'm Edna._ _____

Sam: Hi, Edna. I'm Sam.

Edna: _____

Sam: It's nice to meet you, too.

Edna: _____

Sam: No, I'm not. I'm a teacher.

Edna: _____

Sam: What do you do, Edna?

Edna: _____

Sam: Really? Where do you work?

Edna: _____

Sam: That's great!

Lesson 10: Writing

A Read the Writing Skill. Circle the capital letters at the beginning of sentences. Then circle the periods.

1. (M)s. Lin is a nurse at a nursing home(.)

2. Linda and Max work at a factory.

3. Fara is a caregiver at a hospital.

4. We are servers. We work at a restaurant on Main Street.

5. Matt is a carpenter. He works at the construction site.

> **Writing Skill: Use a period**
>
> Begin a sentence with a capital letter. End a sentence with a period.
>
> (M)y sister works at a hospital(.)

B Look at the picture. Complete the sentences.

Nan
Smith

_____ Smith is my friend. She's a _____

She works at _____ She likes her job.

C Read the text. Correct two errors with capital letters and periods.

Jack is my co-worker. We are stock clerks at Good Food Supermarket It's a hard job. jack lives in New York. I live in New York, too.

Lesson 11: Soft Skills at Work

A BE A GOOD LISTENER. How can you be a good listener at work? Check (✓) the correct answers.

❏ **a.** ask the person to repeat the information

❏ **b.** repeat the information

❏ **c.** talk when another person talks

❏ **d.** follow instructions

Fredy is a painter.
He paints homes.

B Fredy talks to his supervisor. Cross out the incorrect words.
Then circle the best answer.

1. Supervisor: So, put these boxes away first. Then get the new boxes off the truck.

    Fredy: I'm **understand / sorry**. Could you please **repeat / too** that?

    Supervisor: Sure. First these boxes, and then the ones on the truck.

    Fredy: OK, I **do / understand**. Thank you.

2. Fredy _____ when he doesn't understand.
    a. asks a question   **b.** repeats the information

C Fredy talks to a co-worker. Cross out the incorrect words.
Then circle the best answer.

1. Co-worker: Who's **that / those**? Is that the landscaper?

    Fredy: No, she **is / isn't**. She's the electrician.

    Co-worker: Sorry. She is the electrician, right?

    Fredy: Yes, that's **right / nice**. She **work / works** at Main Electric.

2. The co-worker _____ when he doesn't understand.
    a. follows instructions   **b.** repeats the information

D JOB AWARENESS. Fredy is a painter. He has a lot of different customers.
Each customer gives him a different project. Each customer wants different things.
Choose the correct answers.

1. Painters have lots of different projects.   True   False

2. It is important for painters to be good listeners.   True   False

Lesson 1: Vocabulary

A Look at the desk. Write the words.

| a folder | a dictionary | a phone | an eraser |
| a piece of paper | a book | a sticky note | ~~a notebook~~ |

1. _____a notebook_____   2. _____

3. _____   4. _____

5. _____   6. _____

7. _____   8. _____

B Look at the classroom. Write the words.

| a backpack | a laptop | a three-ring binder | a board | a projector | ~~a desk~~ |

1. _____a desk_____

2. _____

3. _____

4. _____

5. _____

6. _____

C Look at the pictures. Complete the sentences

1. I have _a notebook_. I need _a pencil_.

2. I have _____. I need _____.

3. I have _____. I need _____.

4. I have _____. I need _____.

Lessons 2 & 3: Listening and Grammar

A Complete the sentences. Use the words in the box.

| borrow | take out | put away | turn off | ~~write~~ |

1. _____*Write*_____ in your notebooks.

2. _____ a piece of paper.

3. _____ your cell phone.

4. _____ your books.

5. Can I _____ a pen?

B Rewrite the sentences in the negative. Use contractions.

1. Look at the book.

   _*Don't look at the book.*_____

2. Write your name.

   _____

3. Open your dictionary.

   _____

4. Take out your notebook.

   _____

5. Use a pencil.

   _____

6. Put away your book.

   _____

C Match the sentences with the pictures. Write one sentence.

Fill in the circles.	Don't take out your notebook.
~~Don't use a pen.~~	Don't look at your classmate's test.
Take out your book.	Use a pencil.
Don't turn off your computer.	Use a dictionary.

1. _Don't use a pen._

2. _____

3. _____

4. _____

5. _____

6. _____

7. _____

8. _____

Lesson 4: Reading

A DEVELOP YOUR ACADEMIC SKILLS. **Read the Academic Skill.**
Look at the headings in the reading. Complete the sentences.

1. The topic of *Listening Tips* will be how to _____.
   a. improve your listening
   b. speak clearly
   c. be a good reader

2. The topic of *Let's Talk* will be how to _____.
   a. speak correctly
   b. get practice speaking
   c. listen better

> **Academic Skill: Use headings**
>
> Headings are titles for each part of a reading. Before you read an article, look at the headings. They can help you understand the article.

B ▶ Listen and read.

BEST WAYS TO LEARN A LANGUAGE

It can be difficult to learn a language. Learning any language includes four skills: listening, speaking, reading, and writing. Practice all four skills.

Listening Tips
5 Listening to a language all the time helps people to learn a language. Do you like music? Watch a music video. How about movies or TV? Watch a movie with the subtitles turned on. Listen to a podcast online. Find something you like and listen to it.

Read, Read, Read
10 What are you interested in? Do you like fashion, or cars, or food? Find something that you like and read as often as you can.

Let's Talk
Speaking can be difficult to practice. You can use apps to speak with other learners. Find native speakers and talk to them!

15 *Write Away!*
Write about your day. Write about a place or an experience. As your writing improves, start writing longer journals.

C CITE EVIDENCE. **Complete the sentences. Where is the information?**
Write the line number.

Lines

1. There are _____ different language skills.
   a. two   **b.** three   **c.** four   _____

2. When you watch a movie, you should _____.
   a. listen to the music   **b.** read the podcast   **c.** turn on the subtitles   _____

3. Practice writing by keeping a journal about _____.
   a. your phone   **b.** things you do   **c.** your homework   _____

Lessons 5 & 6: Listening and Grammar

A Look at the pictures. Complete the sentences. Use *This*, *That*, *These*, or *Those*.

1. ___This___ is a great mouse.

2. _____ are my pens.

3. _____ are good markers.

4. _____ is a great computer.

B Rewrite the sentences. Change the sentences to plural.

1. That's a great backpack.   _Those are great backpacks._

2. This is a good marker.   _____

3. That's my book.   _____

4. This is a great keyboard.   _____

5. This is my binder.   _____

6. That's a good printer.   _____

C Look at the pictures. Complete the sentences. Use *This*, *That*, *These*, or *Those* and *is* or *are*.

1. ___That is___ your ___computer___.

2. _____ great _____.

3. _____ my _____.

4. _____ great _____.

D Look at the pictures. Complete the questions and answers.

1. **A:** ___Is this___ a screen?

   B: _Yes, it is._

2. **A:** _____ a tablet?

   B: _____

3. **A:** _____ a laptop?

   B: _____

4. **A:** _____ markers?

   B: _____

5. **A:** _____ erasers?

   B: _____

6. **A:** _____ a phone?

   B: _____

E Answer the questions. Circle the letter of the correct answer.

1. What's this called in English?

   a. These are desks.　　**b.** They're desks.　　**c.** It's a desk.

2. What's that called in English?

   a. It's a keyboard.　　**b.** Those are keyboards.　　**c.** These are keyboards.

3. What are these called in English?

   a. That's a sticky note.　　**b.** Those are sticky notes.　　**c.** They're sticky notes.

4. What are those called in English?

   a. That's a marker.　　**b.** They're markers.　　**c.** It's a marker.

5. Is this a mouse?

   a. Yes, they are.　　**b.** Yes, this is.　　**c.** Yes, it is.

6. Is that a screen?

   a. Yes, it is.　　**b.** Yes, this is.　　**c.** Yes, they are.

7. Are those new folders?

   a. Yes, those are.　　**b.** Yes, they are.　　**c.** Yes, it is.

Lesson 7: Workplace, Life, and Community Skills

A Look at the floor plan. Then complete the conversations about the building.

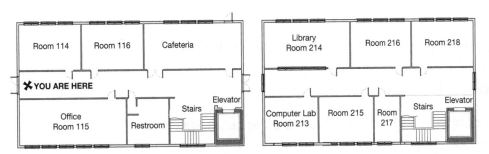

1. **A:** Excuse me. Where is _____the restroom_____?

   B: It's on the right, across from the cafeteria.

2. **A:** Where is _____?

   B: It's on the left, across from the stairs.

3. **A:** Where is _____?

   B: It's across from the office, next to Room 116.

4. **A:** Which way is _____?

   B: It's upstairs, Room 213. It's across from the library.

5. **A:** Which way is _____?

   B: It's upstairs next to the library.

B Look at the floor plan in Exercise A. Answer the questions.

1. Where's Room 114?

   _It's across from the office_____.
   (across from)

2. Where's the cafeteria?

   _____.
   (next to)

3. Where's the elevator?

   _____.
   (across from)

DIRECTORY

		Room
Cafeteria	_ _ _ _ _ _ _ _ _ _	1. _17_
Computer Lab	_ _ _ _ _ _ _ _	2. _____
Library	_ _ _ _ _ _ _ _ _ _	3. _____
Main Office	_ _ _ _ _ _ _ _ _	4. _____

C ▶ Listen. Complete the directory.

Lessons 8 & 9: Listening and Grammar

A Complete the conversations. Use *him* or *her*.

1. **A:** Where's the office?

   B: I don't know. That's Ms. Kramer. She's the director. Ask ____her____.

2. **A:** Where's the elevator?

   B: I don't know. That's Mr. Yu. He's the custodian. Ask _____.

3. **A:** Is the library upstairs?

   B: I don't know. That's Mrs. Conan. She's the librarian. Ask _____.

4. **A:** Is the computer lab open?

   B: I don't know. That's Paul. He's the computer lab assistant. Ask _____.

5. **A:** Where's the ESL office?

   B: I don't know. That's Miss White. She's the office assistant. Ask _____.

B Rewrite the sentences. Change the underlined word or words to *him*, *her*, *it*, or *them*.

1. Please call <u>Rosa</u>.   *Please call her.*

2. Don't open <u>the book</u>.   _____

3. Please help <u>Ramon and Silvia</u>. _____

4. How do you spell <u>your name</u>?   _____

5. Call <u>Ms. Hand</u> about the job.   _____

6. Ask <u>Mr. Duval</u> for help.   _____

C Complete the sentences. Use *me, him, her, us, them, you,* or *it.*

1. I'm at home today. Please call ___me___.

2. Marco is talking. Please don't interrupt _____.

3. Please close your books. Don't use _____ now.

4. Ms. Santos is our teacher. We like _____.

5. We're new students. We have a question. Can you help _____?

6. The students are absent. Can you call _____?

7. The book is interesting. Read _____.

8. They're new students. Please talk to _____.

9. Are you the office assistant? Can I ask _____ a question?

10. We don't understand. Please help _____.

D Complete the conversation. Use the sentences in the box.

~~Can you help me?~~	It's down the hall on the left, Room 24.
That's Mr. Smith, the custodian.	What room is the ESL office?

Bob: Excuse me. *Can you help me?*

Meg: Sure.

Bob: _____

Meg: Sorry. I don't know. Ask him.

Bob: Uh...who's he?

Meg: _____

Bob: Excuse me. Which way is the ESL office?

Mr. Smith: _____

Bob: Thank you.

Mr. Smith: You're welcome.

E ▶ Listen. Check your answers to Exercise D.

Lesson 10: Writing

A Read the Writing Skill. Then circle the verbs.

1. Those (are) new laptops.

2. We have 18 desks in our classroom.

3. He works as a nurse at a hospital.

4. The computer lab is across from the office.

5. Please put away your phones.

6. These computers are old.

7. The office is open at 9.

8. They have new laptops in their office.

> **Writing Skill : Recognize and use verbs**
> Every sentence has a verb. For example:
> I (have) a new tablet.

B Read. Underline the verbs.

I practice English at work. I work at a computer store three days a week. I listen to the manager. I speak with my co-workers. This gives me practice speaking English. I also study. After work I have English class. I do my homework during my break. Sometimes my co-workers help me.

C Read the text. Correct three errors with verbs.

I study English at school three mornings a week. First, we read our books. We answers the questions in the book. I write the new words. We talk about the reading. Then we listen to the teacher and he answer our questions. We listens to a podcast. I get a lot of practice with English in my class.

Lesson 11: Soft Skills at Work

Ying works in a restaurant. She is a server.

A BE FLEXIBLE. Cross out the incorrect words.

A person who is flexible **likes / doesn't like** to change.

B Ying asks a co-worker a question. Cross out the incorrect words. Then circle *True* or *False*.

1. Ying: Do you **work / works** next Saturday?

Co-worker: No, I **do / don't**.

Ying: OK. **Can't / Can** you work that Saturday? I can't **work / works**.

Co-worker: Yes, I **can / work**. No problem.

Ying: Thank you!

2. Ying's co-worker is flexible.   True   False

C Ying talks with another co-worker. Cross out the incorrect words. Then circle *True* or *False*.

1. Co-worker: Hi Ying. Is **these / this** your pen?

Ying: Yes, it **is / are**.

Co-worker: Can I **borrow / put away** it?

Ying: Sure, here you go. I can use a different one.

2. Ying is flexible with her co-worker.   True   False

D JOB INFORMATION. Ying is a server. Look at the job information. Choose the correct answers.

Work Environment	Restaurants
Education Required	No formal education required
Training	On-the-job

1. *Work environment* means when you work.   True   False

2. Servers get training at work.   True   False

Lesson 1: Vocabulary

A Complete the words for family members.

1. p _a_ r _e_ n _t_ s
2. hu ___ b ___ n ___
3. d ___ ug ___ t ___ r
4. s ___ st ___ r
5. c ___ i ___ dr ___ n
6. ___ o ___ he ___

7. ___ if ___
8. b ___ ot ___ e ___
9. ___ on
10. g ___ a ___ df ___ t ___ e ___
11. gr ___ n ___ m ___ t ___ er
12. fat ___ ___ r

B Write the family words from Exercise A in the correct column of the chart.

Male

_____father_____

_____

_____

_____

_____

Female

_____mother_____

_____

_____

_____

_____

Male and Female

_____parents_____

_____

C Look at Dan's family tree. Write sentences about Dan's family.

children	daughter	father	mother
~~parents~~	son	wife	

1. _They're Dan's parents._
2. _____
3. _____
4. _____
5. _____
6. _____
7. _____

Dan

D Look at the pictures. Write sentences about Dan's family.

1. ___He's___ my ___brother___.
2. _____ my _____.

3. _____ my _____.
4. _____ my _____.

Lessons 2 & 3: Listening and Grammar

A Complete the sentences. Use *my, our, your, his, her,* or *their*.

1. I'm Jack. __My__ last name is Hoyt.

2. You're in English 201. _____ teacher is Ms. Rand.

3. He's Ben. _____ last name is Hart.

4. She's from Chile. _____ family is in Miami.

5. The nurses are in the cafeteria. _____ laptops are here.

6. We're new students. Where is _____ classroom?

B Complete the sentences. Cross out the incorrect words.

1. Edna is from Haiti. She looks like **her / ~~their~~** sister.

2. Ivan and Oleg are brothers. **Their / His** parents are in Russia.

3. Marisa and **his / her** husband live in Brazil, but **his / their** children live in Los Angeles.

4. We're servers. The restaurant is across from **his / our** house.

5. Felix looks like **their / his** sister. They live with **our / their** parents.

6. Carlos and I are accountants. **Their / Our** office is across the street.

C Complete the paragraph. Write the correct possessive adjectives.

This is a picture of ___my___ aunt and uncle, and these
           1. (my / your)

are _____ children.
 2. (our / their)

Myra looks like _____ mother. Amit looks like _____ father.
      3. (his / her)   **4. (his / her)**

And Rohan looks like _____ father and _____ mother.
      5. (our / his)   **6. (our / his)**

D Look at Jack's family tree. Complete the sentences.

1. **A:** Who's Molly?

   B: She's _____Jack's_____ cousin.

2. **A:** Who's Monica?

   B: She's _____ wife.

3. **A:** Who's Stanley?

   B: He's _____ husband.

4. **A:** Who's Marie?

   B: She's _____ mother.

5. **A:** Who's Frank?

   B: He's _____ brother.

Stanley   Monica   Uncle Frank   Aunt Marie

Jack

Molly

E Complete the conversation. Use the sentences in the box.

Fran looks like her.	He looks like your mother, too.
She looks nice. Is that your mother?	~~That's my sister, Fran.~~

Eva: That's a great photo. Who's that?

Tom: _That's my sister, Fran._____

Eva: _____

Tom: Yes, it is.

Eva: _____

Tom: Yes. And this is my brother, Tim.

Eva: _____

Tom: I know. And I look like my father.

F ▶ Listen and check your answers.

Lesson 4: Reading

A DEVELOP YOUR ACADEMIC SKILLS. Read the Academic Skill. Complete the sentences.

1. When we make connections, we think about _____.
   a. our experiences   **b.** our education

2. If we make connections when we read, it helps us to _____.
   a. understand better   **b.** read more quickly

> **Academic Skill: Make connections**
>
> When you read, try to make connections between the article and your own life.

B ▶ Listen and read.

MULTIGENERATIONAL FAMILIES

In many homes in the U.S., children live with their parents. Sometimes, children live with their parents and their grandparents. This is a multigenerational family. It means there are many generations in one home.

5 Why do people do this? It is hard for older people to live alone. It is hard for them to take care of a home. They can be lonely if it is hard for them to leave home. Sometimes a family member is sick. It is easier to take care of them if they live with you.

It can save a family money to live together, too. You only pay
10 for one home, not two. Another reason is childcare. Both parents work in many families. A grandparent can help take care of the children.

One-in-five Americans live in a multigenerational household

% of population in multigenerational households

1950	1960	1970	1980	1990	2000	2009	2016
21%	15%	13%	12%	14%	15%	17%	20%

Source: U.S. Census Bureau

C CITE EVIDENCE. Complete the sentences. Where is the information? Write the line number.

Lines

1. The word *multigenerational* means _____.
   a. many generations   **b.** parents and children   **c.** many cousins   _____

2. One reason for multigenerational households is that a family member might be _____.
   a. sick   **b.** happy   **c.** interesting   _____

3. A multigenerational household can be helpful to _____ who work.
   a. children   **b.** parents   **c.** grandchildren   _____

D INTERPRET. Complete the sentences about the bar graph.

1. In 2016, about _____ of people in the United States lived in multigenerational families.
   a. 12%   **b.** 20%   **c.** 17%

2. From 2000 to 2016, the number of people living in multigenerational families increased by _____.
   a. 7%   **b.** 5%   **c.** 9%

Lessons 5 & 6: Listening and Grammar

A Complete the sentences. Use the correct form of *have* or *be*.

1. Tom ___*has*___ a beard.

2. Mia _____ average height.

3. You aren't heavy. You _____ thin.

4. I _____ short and thin. I _____ short hair.

5. Sue _____ tall and thin. She _____ long hair.

6. Bill _____ heavy, and he _____ a mustache.

7. Bob and Pat _____ brothers. They both _____ long hair.

B Complete the sentences. Use contractions when possible.

1. She'___*s*___ short. She ___*has*___ short hair.

2. He _____ a beard. He _____ tall.

3. He _____ short. He _____ a mustache.

4. She _____ tall. She _____ long hair.

5. He _____ heavy. He _____ short hair.

C Look at Exercise B. Match the pictures with the sentences.

___   ___   ___   _1_   ___

D Look at the picture. Describe the people. Write sentences.

Pat

Sam

Al

1. _Pat is short and average weight. He has short hair._

2. _____

3. _____

E Complete the conversation. Use the sentences in the box.

Does he look like you?	Does she look like you?
~~Is your family here in this country?~~	What's your brother like?

Mary: _Is your family here in this country?_

Luz: Well, my brother and sister are here. My parents are in Mexico.

Mary: _____

Luz: He's great.

Mary: _____

Luz: Yes. He's tall and thin and has short hair.

Mary: What about your sister? _____

Luz: No. She's average height and heavy. She has long hair.

F ▶ Listen and check your answers.

Lesson 7: Workplace, Life, and Community Skills

A Look at the work calendar. Find the dates of your co-workers' birthdays. Write sentences.

1. _Jay's birthday is March 5._

2. _____

3. _____

4. _____

5. _____

‹ March 2016				⊡ Q +		
S	M	T	W	T	F	S
28	29	1	2	3	4	5 **Jay**
6	7	8 **Sue**	9	10	11	12 **Linda**
13	14	15	16	17	18	19
20 **Dave**	21	22	23 **Jim**	24	25	26

B Here are some American holidays. Match them with the correct dates on the calendar.

● ◐ ● Calendars + ⬆		Day Week **Month** Year			Q Search	
January 2019					‹ Today ›	
Sun	Mon	Tue	Wed	Thu	Fri	Sat
30	31 New Year's Eve	Jan 1 New Year's Day	2	3	4	5
6	7	8	9	10	11	12
13	14	15	16	17	18	19
20	21 Martin Luther Ki…	22	23	24	25	26
27	28	29	30	31	Feb 1	2 Groundhog Day

1. Martin Luther King Day ____

2. New Year's Day ____

3. New Year's Eve ____

a. December 31

b. third Monday in January

c. January 1

C Look at the ID cards. Write the dates of birth.

Identification Card
Name: Marie Chantall
DOB: 3-18-95

1. _March 18, 1995_

Identification Card
Name: Rob Sinclair
DOB: 8-30-78

2. _____

Identification Card
Name: Hin Suk
DOB: 11-29-85

3. _____

Identification Card
Name: Arshad Monad
DOB: 2-08-02

4. _____

Lessons 8 & 9: Listening and Grammar

A Complete the conversations. Use *is* or *are* and a pronoun if necessary.

1. **A:** How old _____*is*_____ your son?

   B: _____*He's*_____ 12.

2. **A:** How old _____ your kids?

   B: Well, Zach _____ two and Brett _____ eight months.

3. **A:** How old _____ your brother?

   B: _____ 23.

4. **A:** How old _____ your grandchildren?

   B: _____ seven and five.

5. **A:** How old _____ Steve's sister?

   B: I don't know. I think _____ around 30.

B ▶ Listen. Complete the ages and grades of the children on the form.

Holt Central School District

Parents
Father: Hernandez, Martin   **Mother:** Hernandez, Anna

Children	Age	Grade
José	___	___
Carmen	___	___
Miguel	___	___

C Read the paragraph about Mike, his sister, and his brother.

Mike is 10 years old. He's in the fifth grade. He is thin. He has long hair. His sister, Christine, is 13. She's in the eighth grade. She's average weight and height. She has short hair. His brother, Brian, is 15. He's in the ninth grade. He's thin and average height. He has long hair.

D Complete the questions and answers about Mike, his sister, and his brother. Use contractions when possible.

1. ___How old is___ Mike?   ___He's___ 10 ___years old___ .
2. ___Is he in___ the fourth grade?   No, ___he isn't. He's in the fifth grade___ .
3. _____ Mike's sister?   _____ 13 _____ .
4. _____ the eighth grade?   Yes, _____ .
5. _____ Mike's brother?   _____ 15 _____ .
6. _____ the tenth grade?   No, _____ .

E Complete the conversation. Use the sentences in the box.

And her son is seven.	How old are they?
~~I'm at my cousin's house.~~	She's in the fourth grade.

Mark: Hi, Nina. Where are you?

Nina: ___I'm at my cousin's house.___ I'm babysitting for her kids.

Mark: Oh, that's nice. _____

Nina: Well, her daughter is nine. _____

_____ He's in the second grade.

F ▶ Listen and check your answers.

Lesson 10: Writing

A Read the Writing Skill. Then read the sentences in the table. Check (✓) the tips that apply to each sentence.

1. Begin a sentence with a capital letter.

2. End a sentence with a period.

3. People and places begin with a capital letter.

4. Months always begin with a capital letter.

> **Writing Skill: Use a capital letter for months**
>
> Months always begin with a capital letter. For example: Ⓐpril

	1	2	3	4
a. My aunt lives in Colombia.	✓	✓	✓	
b. Her name is Ana.				
c. Her birthday is in May.				
d. Ben is from Houston.				
e. His date of birth is March 5, 2008.				

B Read the model. Answer the questions.

My Uncle

My uncle's name is Jack. I think he's around 50 years old. His birthday is in June. He's short and heavy. He has short hair and a mustache. He lives with us. I'm happy about that. He's a lot of fun.

1. How old is Jack? _____

2. When is his birthday? _____

3. What's he like? _____

C Read the text. Correct 4 more errors.

My cousin's name is ~~lee.~~ Lee She is 15 years old She's in the tenth grade. she's tall and thin. She is interesting. Her birthday is in august. She lives in dallas.

Lesson 11: Soft Skills at Work

A SEPARATE WORK AND HOME LIFE. **Look at the activities. Decide if they are** *work* **or** *home life* **activities.**

	Work	Home Life
Take care of a sick child		✓
Answer a call from your manager		
Talk to your friends on the phone		
Go shopping online		

B Hani's daughter calls her at work. Cross out the incorrect words. Then circle *True* or *False*.

1. Daughter: Hi, Mom.

   Hani: Hi, Nadia. Are you OK?

   Daughter: Yes, I'm fine. **Where / How** are you?

   Hani: I'm at work.

   Daughter: Oh, I'm sorry. I know you **can't / can** talk on the phone at work.

   Hani: That's OK. Can we talk at **work / home**?

   Daughter: OK. Bye!

Hani is an accountant. She works in a busy office

2. Hani separates work and home life.　　　True　　　False

C Hani asks a co-worker a question. Cross out the incorrect words. Then circle *True* or *False*.

1. Hani: Can I ask you a question?

   Co-worker: I'm sorry. I'm busy.

   Hani: Are you working on the report?

   Co-worker: **No / Yes**, I'm not. I'm buying shoes for my **son / daughter**. He's eleven.

2. Hani's co-worker separates work and home life.　　　True　　　False

D JOB INFORMATION. **Hani is an accountant. Accountants keep financial records. For example, financial records can be payments a company receives. They can also be payments a company makes. Complete the sentences.**

money　　　　　　organized

1. Accountants need to be _____.

2. Financial records have information about _____.

Lesson 1: Vocabulary

A Look at the pictures. Write the clothing items. Some words are used more than once.

a blouse	a dress	a jacket	jeans	pants	a shirt
shoes	a skirt	sneakers	socks	a sweater	a T-shirt

1. _____a dress_____

_____shoes_____

2. _____

_____

_____

3. _____

_____

_____

4. _____

_____

_____

5. _____

_____

_____

6. _____

_____

_____

B Look at the clothing items in Exercise A. Add descriptions. Use the colors.

black	blue	brown	gray	green	khaki
orange	pink	purple	red	white	yellow

1. _A black dress and yellow shoes_

2. _____

3. _____

4. _____

5. _____

6. _____

C Write new sentences. Use *It's* or *They're*.

1. The shirt is __yellow__.

It's a yellow shirt.

2. The socks are __black__.

They're black socks.

3. The dress is _____.

_____

4. The sneakers are _____.

_____

5. The jacket is _____.

_____

6. The pants are _____.

_____

D What are you wearing today? Use the example below as a model.

I'm wearing a blue shirt and black pants. I'm wearing black shoes and gray socks.

_____

_____

Lessons 2 & 3: Listening and Grammar

A Cross out the incorrect word.

1. Jack ~~need~~ / needs a new jacket.

2. Sun-Li **want** / **wants** a new dress.

3. Sam and Hal **need** / **needs** new sneakers.

4. I **need** / **needs** a new wallet.

5. They **want** / **wants** new pants.

6. You **need** / **needs** a new jacket.

B Write sentences. Use the words in parentheses and *has* or *have*.

1. (Carla / a new watch)

   _Carla has a new watch_____.

2. (Eric / a yellow backpack)

   _____.

3. (I / new shoes)

   _____.

4. (Leo and Mark / new shirts)

   _____.

5. (Matt / a new shirt and jeans)

   _____.

6. (Mr. Lee / black shoes)

   _____.

C Complete the sentences. Use the verbs in parentheses.

1. Wen __wants__ a new shirt and jeans.
   (want)

2. Dan _____ new sneakers.
   (need)

3. Charles _____ a new shirt.
   (have)

4. Tina and Monika _____ new skirts.
   (want)

5. We _____ new jackets.
   (need)

6. I _____ a new handbag.
   (have)

7. Ben _____ new socks.
   (need)

8. My daughters _____ new jeans.
   (have)

9. Paulo and Brian _____ new wallets.
   (want)

Lesson 4: Workplace, Life, and Community Skills

A Count the money. Write the amount.

1. __52¢__   2. _____   3. _____   4. _____

B Look at the price tags. Answer the questions.

$39.95 $49.00 $69.00 $76.00 $110.00

1.   2.   3.   4.   5.

1. **A:** How much ____are the jeans____?

   B: They're ____$39.95____.

2. **A:** How much _____?

   B: _____.

3. **A:** How much _____?

   B: _____.

4. **A:** How much _____?

   B: _____.

5. **A:** How much _____?

   B: _____.

C ▶ Listen. Circle the correct amount.

1. **a.** $34.95   **b.** $24.95   2. **a.** $37.50   **b.** $37.60

3. **a.** $15.99   **b.** $14.99   4. **a.** $5.95   **b.** $9.95

5. **a.** $24.50   **b.** $34.50   6. **a.** $49.95   **b.** $49.99

D Look at the receipt for clothes. Answer the questions.

1. What is the name of the store?

Fashion World

2. What is the date on the receipt?

_____

3. How much is the shirt?

_____

4. How much is the sweater?

_____

5. How much are the jeans?

_____

```
        FASHION WORLD
        587 Fairview Road
      Los Angeles, CA 93940
         (805) 555-3694

09-15-19

MEN'S SHIRT                 15.99
WOMEN'S SWEATER             32.99
WOMEN'S JEANS               25.99

SUBTOTAL                    74.97
TAX (.095)                   7.12

TOTAL                       82.09

CASH AMOUNT PAID            90.00
CHANGE DUE                   7.91

Please keep receipt for returns.
   Thank you for shopping at
        Fashion World.
```

E Look at the receipt. Complete the formulas.

Subtotal	x	Tax Rate	=	Sales Tax
74.97	x	.095	=	_____

Subtotal	+	Sales Tax	=	Total
74.97	+	_____	=	_____

F Look at the table of tax rates. Use the subtotal from Exercise D to calculate the amount of tax for each city. Then calculate the total.

Formula

Subtotal	x	Tax Rate	=	Sales Tax
74.97	x	.095	=	_$7.12_

Tax Rate by City

City	State	Subtotal	Tax Rate (%)	Tax Rate (decimal)	Sales Tax	Total
Los Angeles	California	$74.97	9.50%	**1.** .0950	**2.** $7.12	**3.** $82.09
Chicago	Illinois	$74.97	10.25%	**4.**	**5.**	**6.**
Miami	Florida	$74.97	7%	**7.**	**8.**	**9.**

Lessons 5 & 6: Listening and Grammar

A Complete the conversations with *do* or *does*.

1. **A:** _____Do_____ you have this in blue?

   B: Yes, we ___do___.

2. **A:** _____ Jim need a backpack?

   B: Yes, he _____.

3. **A:** _____ Sara like this jacket?

   B: No, she _____.

4. **A:** _____ the boys want new sneakers?

   B: Yes, they _____.

5. **A:** _____ you need a new jacket?

   B: No, I _____.

6. **A:** _____ Mark and Eric need new jeans?

   B: No, they _____.

B Unscramble the words to form questions.

1. _Do you have this sweater in a large?_
   (have / you / sweater / large / in / do / this / a)

2. _____
   (she / want / does / this / medium / a / T-shirt / in)

3. _____
   (Tom / jacket / have / does / a / black)

4. _____
   (do / like / these / you / shoes)

5. _____
   (blue / you / skirt / have / this / in / do)

6. _____
   (dress / medium / a / do / have / this / you / in)

C Use *do*, *does*, *don't*, or *doesn't* and the correct form of the verbs in parentheses.

1. **A:** ___Do___ you ___have___ this jacket in a small?
   (have)

   B: Yes, we ___do___. Here you go.

2. **A:** _____ he _____ a new wallet?
   (need)

   B: No, he _____. He _____ a wallet.
   (have)

3. **A:** _____ you _____ this watch?
   (like)

   B: Yes, I _____. It's a great watch.

4. **A:** _____ they _____ new shoes for school?
   (need)

   B: No, they _____.They _____ shoes.
   (have)

5. **A:** _____ Monica _____ new sneakers?
   (want)

   B: Yes, she _____. She _____ these sneakers.
   (like)

6. **A:** _____ they _____ this sweater in a large?
   (have)

   B: No, they _____. They _____ a small and a medium.
   (have)

D ▶ Listen. Answer the questions.

1. Does Linda need new clothes?   ___Yes, she does.___
2. Does she need T-shirts?   _____
3. Does she like the green T-shirts? _____
4. Does Linda need pants?   _____
5. Does Linda like the blue pants? _____
6. Do they have the pants in a small? _____
7. Does she like the jacket?   _____

Lesson 7: Reading

A Listen and read.

A CASHLESS SOCIETY

Today, more people use credit cards. One day, we may not use cash. That is a cashless society. Is this a good or a bad thing?

Some people say that it is good. A cashless society is safer. If people don't have cash, people can't steal it. Second, you have credit card receipts of what you buy. This means you can see what you spend each month.

5 Other people think that it is not good. Sometimes there are problems with technology. Then people can't buy things that they need. Second, people can use technology to steal your credit card information. This can happen when you shop online or in a store. They can steal other information about you. This can be dangerous. They can use this information to get new credit cards in your name.

In conclusion, there are good things and bad things about credit cards. But they aren't going away any time soon.

B DEVELOP YOUR ACADEMIC SKILLS. **Read the Academic Skill. Complete the sentence.**

1. The writer says, "people can't steal it."

   You can infer the writer thinks credit cards
   are _____ than cash.
   a. better
   b. worse

Academic Skill: Make inferences

You make inferences about things the writer is thinking but doesn't say.

C CITE EVIDENCE. **Cross out the incorrect words. Where is the information? Write the line number.**

Lines

1. Today, more people use **a credit card / cash**. _____

2. One bad thing about **a credit card / cash** is that there isn't a receipt
   for everything that you buy. _____

3. One bad thing about **a credit card / cash** is that technology might
   cause problems with using it. _____

Lessons 8 & 9: Listening and Grammar

A Complete the sentences. Use *don't* or *doesn't*.

1. They ___don't___ fit.

2. He _____ like it.

3. They _____ match.

4. It _____ fit.

5. They _____ want them.

6. The zipper _____ work.

B Complete the sentences with *don't* or *doesn't* and the underlined verb.

1. You <u>need</u> a new sweater. You ___don't need___ a new shirt.

2. I <u>like</u> the blue jacket. I _____ the black jacket.

3. He <u>likes</u> the blue sneakers. He _____ the red sneakers.

4. The black shirt <u>fits</u>. The blue shirt _____.

5. They <u>want</u> new jeans. They _____ new shoes.

6. She <u>needs</u> a new skirt. She _____ a new blouse.

C Rewrite the sentences in the negative. Use contractions.

1. He likes the red jacket.　　　*He doesn't like the red jacket.*

2. She wants the orange sneakers.　　　_____

3. They need new jeans.　　　_____

4. I have my receipt.　　　_____

5. These pants fit.　　　_____

6. This jacket fits.　　　_____

7. She has a brown backpack.　　　_____

D Look at the return form. The customer is returning clothes. Write the reasons. Use contractions.

1. *The shirt doesn't fit.*　　　　　　**2.** _____

3. _____　　　　　　**4.** _____

Return / Refund Information

Name __Paula Gusto__　　　Phone __(310)555-9877__

Address __423 Plainview Road__

__Santa Monica, CA 90403__

Merchandise Returned

	Item	Item number	Color	Size	Price	Reason
1.	Shirt	F56006	Blue	S	$29.95	R1
2.	Watch	M32085	Brown		$39.95	R3
3.	Jacket	S42008	Red	M	$69.95	R4
4.	Dress	K3107	White	L	$59.95	R1

Reasons
R1: Doesn't fit **R2:** Doesn't match **R3:** Doesn't work **R4:** Don't like **R5:** Other

Lesson 10: Writing

(A) Read the Writing Skill. Add commas.

1. He needs a new jacket, pants, and jeans.
2. Jack wants a new shirt jeans and socks for his birthday.
3. She has a new skirt blouse and shoes.
4. I wear pants a white shirt and black shoes to work.
5. Mia wants a new dress a skirt and a blouse for her birthday.

> **Writing Skill: Use commas in a list**
> Use commas between words in a list. For example:
> I wear a shirt, pants, and shoes at work.

(B) Look at the pictures. Add commas to the sentences.

My name is Hector. I'm a server at a restaurant. At work, I wear a blue shirt khaki pants and brown shoes. At home, I wear a T-shirt blue jeans and sneakers.

(C) Read the text. Correct two errors with commas.

It's my brother's birthday tomorrow. He wants a new shirt, jeans and a T-shirt. He needs a new jacket pants, and shoes.

Lesson 11: Soft Skills at Work

A BE PROFESSIONAL. How can you be professional? Check (✓) the correct answers.

☐ **a.** help co-workers

☐ **b.** always put the customer first

☐ **c.** always be polite to customers

☐ **d.** stay calm at work

Loc works at a store. He's a cashier.

B A customer asks Loc a question. Cross out the incorrect words. Then circle *True* or *False*.

1. Customer: I **need / needs** to ask you a question.

Loc: Sure.

Customer: I **want / wants** this sweater in blue.

Loc: It's a nice sweater.

Customer: **Do / Does** you have it?

Loc: Yes, we **do / don't**. Let me find a sales assistant to help you.

2. Loc is professional.   True   False

C Loc talks with a co-worker. Cross out the incorrect words. Then circle *True* or *False*.

1. Co-worker: Everyone **wants / needs** to use credit cards.

Loc: Is that a problem?

Co-worker: It **take / takes** a long time!

Loc: Do you **need / needs** help?

Co-worker: No, I **do / don't**. The customers will have to wait!

Loc: I can help you, if you **wants / want**.

2. Loc's co-worker is professional.   True   False

D JOB INFORMATION. Loc is a cashier. Read the information. Choose the correct answers.

Work Environment	Stores
Education Required	No experience required
Training	On-the-job

1. Cashiers need work experience.   True   False

2. Cashiers get training.   True   False

Lesson 1: Vocabulary

A Cross out the word that doesn't belong.

1. bathtub   toilet   ~~sofa~~   shower

2. table   chair   closet   dresser

3. kitchen   sink   bathroom   bedroom

4. microwave   stove   bed   refrigerator

5. dresser   shower   closet   bed

B Look at the pictures. Complete the sentences.

1. We need a new ___microwave___.

2. Mrs. Sanchez wants a new _____.

3. Mia needs a new _____.

4. Mr. Cho wants a new _____.

5. Angela needs a new _____.

6. I need a new _____.

C Look at the pictures and the floor plan. Complete the sentences.

1.

Please put the ___lamp___ on the table in the ___bedroom___.

2.

Please put the _____ next to the closet in the _____.

3.

Please put the _____ across from the refrigerator in the _____.

4.

Please put the _____ next to the table in the _____.

5.

Please put the _____ next to the sofa in the _____.

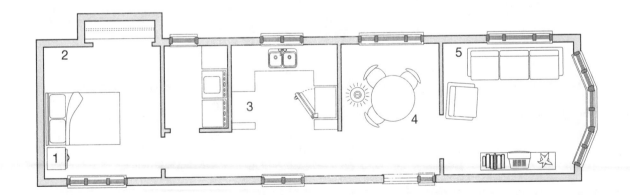

Lessons 2 & 3: Listening and Grammar

A Complete the paragraphs. Use *there's* or *there are*.

1. ___There's___ a living room, and ___there's___ a small kitchen.

   _____ no dining room. _____ two bedrooms, but _____ no laundry room.

   _____ one bathroom. _____ a garage. _____ no closet.

2. _____ a large living room, and _____ a large kitchen, too.

   _____ a small dining room. _____ two bathrooms and three bedrooms.

   _____ two closets, also. _____ a laundry room, but _____ no garage.

3. _____ a large living room, but _____ no dining room.

   _____ one bedroom. _____ one bathroom, but _____ no closets.

   _____ a kitchen, and _____ a garage.

B Read the paragraphs again. Write the paragraph number under each floor plan.

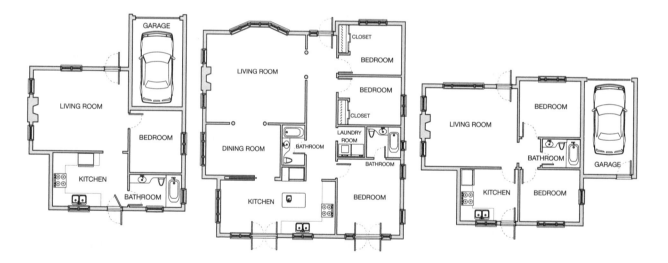

Floor Plan A

Paragraph ___3___

Floor Plan B

Paragraph _____

Floor Plan C

Paragraph _____

C ▶ Listen. Circle the correct picture.

1. a.    b.

2. a.    b.

3. a.
House for Rent!
(\$450)/ month

b.
House for Rent!
(\$2,000)/ month

4. a.    b.

D Look at picture A and read the sentences. Then write sentences about picture B. Use contractions when possible.

chair   lamps   sofa   coffee table

A

B

A. _There's a sofa. There's a coffee table, and there's a chair. There are no lamps._

B. _____

Lesson 4: Reading

A DEVELOP YOUR ACADEMIC SKILLS. Read the Academic Skill.
Then read the statements. Circle *True* or *False*.

1. You only need to read an article once to understand it.

True   False

2. You understand an article better if you read it again.

True   False

B ▶ Listen and read.

HAVE AN EMERGENCY PLAN FOR FIRE SAFETY

In a fire, every second counts! Each room in your home needs two exits. You need two ways out in case of a fire. This way, if one exit is already on fire,
5 you have another way to leave. An exit can be a door or a window. So don't put anything in front of windows or doors. This way, you can exit quickly.

Everyone should practice fire safety.
10 First, make a map of your home. Mark the smoke alarms and the exits. Then practice a home fire drill. Choose a

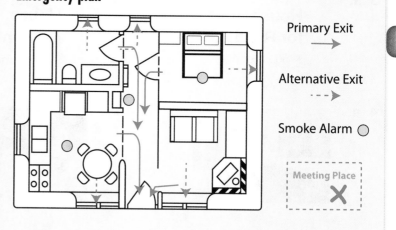

Emergency plan

Primary Exit →

Alternative Exit - - →

Smoke Alarm ○

Meeting Place ✗

meeting place outside. Everyone in the family should meet there. Leave your room. Don't bring anything with you. Your laptop and phone are not important. Just leave! Stay outside until everyone in your family is there.

C CITE EVIDENCE. Read the article again. Cross out the incorrect word in each sentence.

Lines

1. Each room in the house should have two **windows / exits**.   _____

2. An exit can be a door or a **closet / window**.   _____

3. To practice fire safety, first make a map of your **windows / home**.   _____

4. Mark the **bedrooms / exits** on the map.   _____

5. At the end of the fire drill, everyone should go to the **meeting place / kitchen**.   _____

Lessons 5 & 6: Listening and Grammar

A Look at the picture. Make questions and write short answers.

1. _Is there_ a sofa?   _Yes, there is._

2. _____ a dining room?   _____

3. _____ a kitchen table?   _____

4. _____ a refrigerator?   _____

5. _____ chairs?   _____

6. _____ floor lamps?   _____

7. _____ a microwave?   _____

8. _____ a stove?   _____

B Look at the apartment ads. Complete the conversations.

1. **A:** (one-bedroom apartment) _Is there a one-bedroom apartment for rent?_

   B: _Yes, there is. There's a furnished one-bedroom apartment for rent._

   A: (appliances) _____

   B: _____

   A: (bed) _____

   B: _____

   A: (dining room) _____

   B: _____

> **FOR RENT**
> **1-Bedroom Furnished Apartment:**
> large new kitchen, new appliances, 3 closets, new bed, sofa, and table

2. **A:** (two-bedroom apartment) _____

   B: _____

   A: (microwave) _____

   B: _____

   A: (closets) _____

   B: _____

   A: (laundry room) _____

   B: _____

> **FOR RENT**
> **2-Bedroom Unfurnished Apartment:**
> new bathroom, microwave, 4 closets, large living room

Lesson 7: Workplace, Life, and Community Skills

A ▶ Listen. Circle the letter of the correct address.

1. **a.** 365 Meadow Street   **b.** 365 Meadow Drive   **c.** 365 Meadow Avenue

2. **a.** 52 Park Boulevard   **b.** 52 Park Street   **c.** 52 Park Road

3. **a.** 45 Orange Lane   **b.** 45 Orange Avenue   **c.** 45 Orange Road

4. **a.** 37 Sutton Street   **b.** 37 Sutton Avenue   **c.** 37 Sutton Boulevard

5. **a.** 145 Drake Road   **b.** 145 Drake Street   **c.** 145 Drake Avenue

B Write the abbreviations.

1. Street   _St._

2. Drive   _____

3. Avenue   _____

4. Boulevard   _____

5. Road   _____

C Match the parts of the conversations.

1. What's the address?   _c_   **a.** Yes, it does.

2. How much is the apartment?   _____   **b.** No, but the stove is new.

3. Does it have parking?   _____   **c.** It's 3205 Baker Place.

4. Does it have a new kitchen?   _____   **d.** Yes, there is.

5. Is there a laundry room?   _____   **e.** It's $1,200 a month.

D Look at the ad. Write three more descriptions. Do not use abbreviations.

> **FOR RENT**
> 2-BR Apt: Lg Kit, DR,
> A/C, Pkg, Utils. incl.
> $1,800 month

There's a two-bedroom apartment for rent. _____

_____

_____

E ▶ Listen. Complete the notes about the apartments.

1.

FOR RENT

_1_ Bedroom(s)

$ _____ a month

Large _____ with new _____

14 Bank _____, Apt. _____

2.

FOR RENT

____ Bedroom(s) ____ Bathroom(s)

$1,300 a month

Large _____ with new shower

346 Clover _____, Apt. _____

3.

FOR RENT

____ Bedroom(s)

In new _____

$ _____ a month

Large _____

45 Orchard _____, Apt. _____

4.

FOR RENT

____ Bedroom(s)

$ _____ a month

Large _____ _____

_____ room in bldg.

3 Apple _____, Apt. 2A

F GO ONLINE. Look up an online ad for an apartment near you. Write four sentences describing the apartment.

_____

_____

_____

_____

Lessons 8 & 9: Listening and Grammar

A Complete the sentences. Use *from*, *to*, *in*, *at*, or *on*.

1. Carmen is coming __*from*__ work.

2. It's _____ 554 Benson Avenue.

3. The hotel is _____ Greenville.

4. I'm going _____ the store.

5. My office is _____ Main Street.

6. Turn right _____ the third light.

B Complete the conversation. Use *from*, *on*, or *at*.

A: How do I get to Century Manufacturing Company?

B: __*From*__ here? Let me check my phone. Okay. Go east _____ Maple Avenue. Turn left _____ Bank Street. Then continue _____ Bank Street to 6th Street. It's _____ the corner of Bank and 6th.

C Complete the conversation. Use *from*, *to*, *in*, *at*, or *on*.

Sam: Hi, Jess. Are you coming __*to*__ my office?

Jess: Yes, Sam. How do I get there _____ here? I'm coming _____ work.

Sam: My office is _____ Oakdale. First, go _____ Conner Street. Turn left. Continue north _____ Conner Street. Then turn left _____ the light. That's Manor Road. My office is _____ 58 Manor Road.

Jess: Great!

D ▶ Listen. Cross out the incorrect words.

Go (~~south~~ / **north**) (**in** / **on**) Powell Street. Continue (**at** / **on**) Powell Street for three blocks. Turn right (**on** / **at**) the (**3rd** / **2nd**) light. Continue (**east** / **west**) (**in** / **on**) Starrett Street. Our store is (**at** / **on**) Starrett Street (**in** / **on**) the (**left** / **right**). It's (**at** / **in**) 3228 Starrett Street.

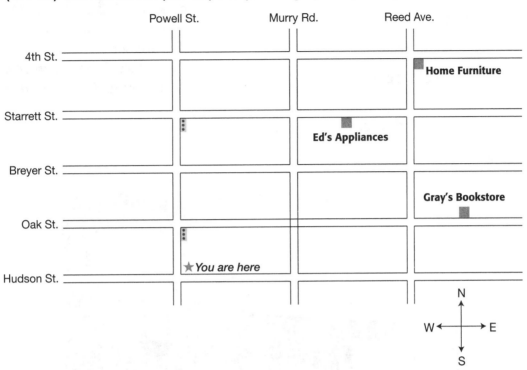

E Look at the map. You are at the corner of Powell and Hudson. Read the directions in Exercise D. Where are you?

I'm at _____.

F Look at the map in Exercise D. You are at the corner of 4th and Powell. Complete the directions to Gray's Bookstore.

Go _____*south*_____ _____ Powell Street. Continue _____ Powell Street for one block. Turn left _____ the light. Continue _____ Starrett Street for two blocks. Go _____ on Reed Avenue. Continue _____ Reed Avenue for two blocks. Turn _____ on Oak Street. It's _____ 4118 Oak Street.

Lesson 10: Writing

A Read the Writing Skill. Then circle the details.

1. There is a (large) (sunny) room.

2. There are two small windows.

3. There is a nice lamp.

4. There is a big new microwave.

5. There is a small old table.

> **Writing Skill: Use details**
>
> Put details in your writing.
> For example:
> **No details:** There are windows.
> **With details:** There are (three) (big) windows.

B Look at the picture. Add details.

big lamp small sunny table window

My favorite room at home is the living room. It's big and _____.

There is a _____. There's a _____ couch and a _____ table.

There's a _____ next to the _____. The best part is the couch.

C Read the text. Correct two errors with *there is / there are.*

My favorite room at home is the bedroom. It's big and sunny. There is three windows. There's a large closet, and there a new dresser. There's a large lamp next to a small table.

Lesson 11: Soft Skills at Work

A FIND INFORMATION. Cross out the incorrect words.

A person who is good at finding information

gets / doesn't get answers to important questions.

This is Milos. He's an assistant building manager.

B Milos talks to a renter in his building. Cross out the incorrect words.
Then circle *True* or *False*.

1. Milos: Ms. Hand **need / needs** a new microwave. Do we have one?

Building manager: I'm not sure, Milos.

Milos: I can check downstairs. There **are / is** many appliance boxes there.

Building manager: That's a good idea. Thanks, Milos.

2. Milos is finding information. True   False

C Milos talks to someone about an apartment. Cross out the incorrect words.
Then circle *True* or *False*.

1. Renter: Hi. Are you the building manager?

Milos: No, **I'm not / he's not**. He's not here right now. Can I help you?

Renter: We want to see the **one-bedroom apartment / kitchen**.

Milos: I think it's still available. Let me call the manager to see.

2. Milos is finding information. True   False

D JOB INFORMATION. Milos is an assistant building manager. He gets calls about
problems in the building. Sometimes he fixes things. When he can't fix something,
he calls an expert to fix it. Choose the correct answers.

1. Assistant building managers need to be able to fix anything.   True   False

2. Assistant building managers talk with renters.   True   False

Unit 7: Day After Day

Lesson 1: Vocabulary

A Complete the activities. Use the words in the box.

breakfast ~~the dishes~~ dressed a shower homework to work

1. wash _____*the dishes*_____

2. eat _____

3. go _____

4. take _____

5. get _____

6. do _____

B Look at Tara's schedule for the evening. Complete the sentences.

1. She _____*gets home*_____ at 5:30.

2. She _____ from 6:00 to 7:00.

3. She _____ at 7:00.

4. At 7:30, she _____.

5. At 8:00, she _____ and _____.

6. From 8:30 to 9:30, she _____.

7. She _____ at 9:30.

8. At 10:00, she _____.

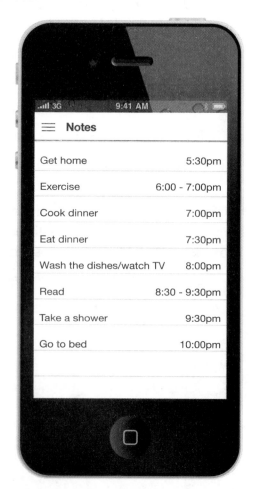

3G	9:41 AM	
☰ **Notes**		
Get home		5:30pm
Exercise		6:00 - 7:00pm
Cook dinner		7:00pm
Eat dinner		7:30pm
Wash the dishes/watch TV		8:00pm
Read		8:30 - 9:30pm
Take a shower		9:30pm
Go to bed		10:00pm

C Look at the pictures. Complete the conversations.

5:00 am

1. **A:** What time does Max ____get up____?

   B: At ___5:00___.

5:15 am

2. **A:** What time does he _____?

   B: At _____.

5:30 am

3. **A:** What time does he _____?

   B: At _____.

5:45 am

4. **A:** What time does he _____?

   B: At _____.

6:00 am

5. **A:** What time does he _____?

   B: At _____.

D Write about yourself. What is your schedule like?

I get up at _____.

I eat breakfast at _____.

I go to **work / school** at _____.

Lesson 2: Listening and Grammar

A Complete the conversations.

1. A: When ___do___ you ___work___? **(work)**   **B:** I work on Saturdays.

2. A: What time _____ she _____? **(get up)**   **B:** She gets up at 7:00.

3. A: When _____ they _____ class? **(have)**   **B:** They have class from 6:00 to 8:00.

4. A: What time _____ you _____ to work? **(go)**   **B:** I go to work at 8:00.

5. A: When _____ the movie _____? **(start)**   **B:** The movie starts at 7:45.

6. A: What time _____ she _____ home? **(get)**   **B:** She gets home at 5:30.

B Make questions with *What time*. Complete the conversations.

6:30pm

1. (you / get home)

   A: _What time do you get home?_

   B: _At 6:30._

7:15am

2. (they / go to work)

   A: _____

   B: _____

12:00pm

3. (Arnold / exercise)

   A: _____

   B: _____

6:00am

4. (she / eat breakfast)

   A: _____

   B: _____

5:30pm

5. (Jason and Marie / eat dinner)

   A: _____

   B: _____

C Complete the conversations. Use *on*, *at*, *from*, or *to*.

1. **A:** When does Maria play soccer?

   B: _From_ 10:00 _to_ 12:00 _on_ Saturdays.

2. **A:** When does Jack take a computer class?

   B: _____ Tuesdays.

3. **A:** When does Paul watch TV?

   B: _____ 8:00 _____ 10:00.

4. **A:** When does your English class start?

   B: _____ 7:00.

5. **A:** When do they get up?

   B: _____ 10:00 _____ Saturdays.

D Look at Sam's schedule. Complete the conversations.

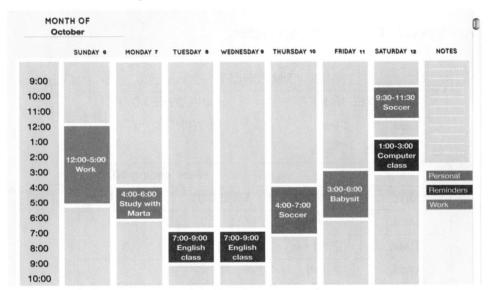

1. **A:** Is Sam free on Sundays at 4:00?

   B: No. _He works on Sundays from 12:00–5:00._

2. **A:** Is he free on Wednesdays at 8:00?

   B: No. _____

3. **A:** Is he free on Thursdays at 6:00?

   B: No. _____

4. **A:** Is he free on Fridays at 5:00?

   B: No. _____

5. **A:** Is he free on Saturdays at 2:00?

   B: No. _____

Lesson 4: Workplace, Life, and Community Skills

A ▶ Listen. Complete the schedule.

SUNDAY 29	MONDAY 30	TUESDAY 1	WEDNESDAY 2	THURSDAY 3	FRIDAY 4	SATURDAY 5
_____	_____	*10:00*	_____	_____	_____	_____
_____	_____	*2:00*	_____	_____	_____	_____
_____	_____	*work*	_____	_____	_____	_____

B Look at the work schedule. Complete the sentences.

TIME SHEET

EMPLOYEE NAME		EMPLOYEE I.D. #
Last	First	5470998
Roberts	Clara	

Week ending 10/15

DAY	TIME IN	TIME OUT	HOURS
Mon.	off		
Tues.	7:00 P.M.	12:00 A.M.	5
Wed.	off		
Thurs.	7:00 P.M.	12:00 A.M.	5
Fri.	off		
Sat.	9:00 A.M.	1:00 P.M.	4
Sun.	6:00 A.M.	12:00 P.M.	6

1. Clara works from ___*7:00 P.M.*___ to ___*12:00 A.M.*___ on ___*Tuesday*___ and ___*Thursday*___.

2. She is off on _____, _____, and _____.

3. She starts work at _____ on Saturday.

4. She finishes work at _____ on Saturday.

5. She works from _____ to _____ on Sunday.

6. She works _____ hours this week.

C Look at the time sheet. Complete the conversations.

1. **A:** When does Martin work?

   B: He works on ___Tuesdays___,

   _____, and _____.

2. **A:** What time does he start work on Tuesdays?

   B: At _____.

3. **A:** When does he work on Thursdays?

   B: He works from _____ to

   _____.

4. **A:** What time does he start work on Saturdays?

   B: At _____.

5. **A:** When does he finish work at 2:00?

   B: On _____.

TIME SHEET

EMPLOYEE NAME		EMPLOYEE I.D. #
Last	First	459-34-9876
Chu, Martin		

Week ending 7/15

DAY	TIME IN	TIME OUT	HOURS
Mon.	off		
Tues.	11:00 A.M.	7:00 P.M.	8
Wed.	off		
Thurs.	11:00 A.M.	7:00 P.M.	8
Fri.	off		
Sat.	8:00 A.M.	2:00 P.M.	6
Sun.	off		

TOTAL HOURS
22

D Look at your schedule on your phone. Write one event for each day of the week. Include the time of the event.

Day	Event	Time
Monday	_____	_____
Tuesday	_____	_____
Wednesday	_____	_____
Thursday	_____	_____
Friday	_____	_____
Saturday	_____	_____
Sunday	_____	_____

Lessons 5 & 6: Listening and Grammar

A Look at the calendar. Complete the sentences. Use *always*, *usually*, *sometimes*, or *never*.

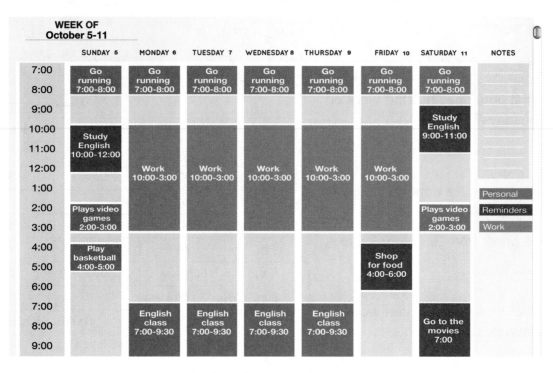

1. Brad _____never_____ goes to the beach on Sundays.

2. He _____ works from 10:00 to 3:00 Mondays to Fridays.

3. He _____ does laundry on Fridays.

4. He _____ goes running in the morning.

5. He _____ goes shopping for food on Fridays.

6. He _____ plays video games in the afternoon.

B Unscramble the words to form sentences.

1. _Sarah usually shops for food on Saturdays._____
   (Sarah / Saturdays / shops for food / usually / on)

2. _____
   (Martin / takes a shower / always / at night)

3. _____
   (Conor / on / rides his bike / Sundays / sometimes)

4. _____
   (they / on / never / do laundry / Sundays)

C Look at the pictures. Complete the conversations.

1. **A:** What does Pedro usually do on Saturdays?

   B: *He usually goes to the park.*

2. **A:** What does Elena sometimes do on Sundays?

   B: _____

3. **A:** What does Mr. Gray always do on Saturdays?

   B: _____

4. **A:** What does Mr. Kim never do on Saturday nights?

   B: _____

5. **A:** What does May-Li sometimes do on Sundays?

   B: _____

6. **A:** What does Teresa always do on Sundays?

   B: _____

D Complete the sentences. Write about your weekend activities.

1. I always _____.

2. I usually _____.

3. I sometimes _____.

4. I never _____.

Lesson 7: Reading

A DEVELOP YOUR ACADEMIC SKILLS. Read the Academic Skill. Make predictions about the article. Look at the heading and chart. Try to guess what people do in their free time. Complete the sentence.

Children in the U.S. probably _____ in their free time.
- **a.** do homework
- **b.** play video games
- **c.** do sports
- **d.** read

> **Academic Skill: Make predictions**
>
> Before you read an article, guess what it will say. Then read to find out: Were your predictions correct?

B Read.

WHAT CHILDREN DO IN THEIR FREE TIME

In the U.S., children usually have free time after 3:00 p.m. They have a lot of free time after that. What do they do? Many children watch TV every day. Some children watch videos on their tablets or phones. Other children play games on their computers or
5 tablets.

Many children also do sports. They meet their friends and play different sports. They also attend religious groups and youth groups. They do this during the week after school or on the weekends. Some children take music lessons. Other children take
10 dance lessons.

Children in the U.S. are very busy after school. They have a lot of free time, but they use it well.

Average hours per day spent in activities

Watch TV	2.4
Play video games	0.9
Read	0.1

Note: Based on data from 15-19 years old.

Source: U.S. Bureau of Labor Statistics

C Look at your prediction in A. Was it correct?   ❑ Yes   ❑ No

D CITE EVIDENCE. Complete the sentences. Where is the information? Write the line number.

Lines

1. Children usually have free time _____.
   - **a.** after 4 p.m.
   - **b.** after 3 p.m.
   - **c.** after 6 p.m.
   _____

2. Many children _____ after school.
   - **a.** read
   - **b.** do homework
   - **c.** watch TV
   _____

3. Children also _____.
   - **a.** play video games
   - **b.** do sports
   - **c.** play music
   _____

E INTERPRET. Look at the bar graph. Complete the sentences.

1. In the U.S., children spent _____ hours a day watching TV in their free time.
   - **a.** 1.9
   - **b.** 2.4
   - **c.** 0.9

2. On average, children spent _____ hours more playing video games than reading every day in their free time.
   - **a.** 0.8
   - **b.** 0.9
   - **c.** 0.1

Lessons 8 & 9: Listening and Grammar

A Complete the questions.

1. How often __does__ Joe __listen to music__? (listen to music)

2. How often _____ you _____? (go running)

3. How often _____ Sam and Mark _____? (play video games)

4. How often _____ your mother _____? (ride her bike)

5. How often _____ Yari _____? (work)

6. How often _____ your friends _____? (have English class)

B ▶ Listen. Check (✓) in the correct columns in the chart.

	Once a week	Three times a week	Every day	Never
Go running		✓		
Take a long walk				
Do puzzles				
Listen to music				

C Complete the sentences about yourself. Use the ideas in the box.

when I go to a party	when I go to school	when I listen to music
when I see my friends	when I take a test	when I watch a sad movie

1. I feel relaxed _____.

2. I feel bored _____.

3. I feel stressed _____.

4. I feel sad _____.

5. I feel happy _____.

6. I feel excited _____.

Lesson 10: Writing

A Read the Writing Skill. Then circle the capital letters in the days of the week.

1. (M)onday is my favorite day. I don't work on (M)ondays.
2. Charlie works on Tuesdays, Thursdays, and Fridays.
3. Jim often relaxes at home on Fridays.
4. Mandy usually works on Saturdays and Sundays.
5. I never work on Friday.

> **Writing Skill: Use a capital letter for days of the week**
> Days of the week begin with capital letters. For example:
> I work on (T)uesdays, (F)ridays, and (S)aturdays.

B Complete the sentences about Ben.

1. On ___Mondays___, Ben usually does laundry.

2. He works on _____, _____, and _____ from 9 to 3.

3. He usually goes running on _____.

4. On _____, he relaxes.

5. On _____, he usually plays basketball.

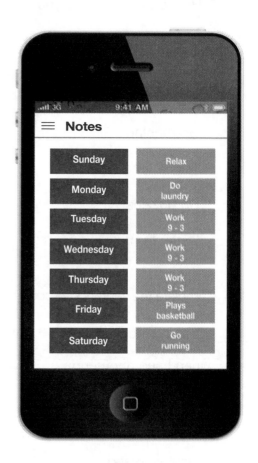

C Read the text. Correct four errors.

My favorite day of the week is saturday. I never work on Saturday. I stay home and spend time with family. I usually play basketball with my brother on the morning. I sometimes meet friends for lunch. I usually go to the movies in night. I love saturday. It's the best day of the week.

Lesson 11: Soft Skills at Work

A BE A TEAM PLAYER. **Complete the sentence.**

A person who is a team player _____.

a. offers to help co-workers

b. focuses on his or her own work

c. gives wrong answers to co-workers

Rita is an office assistant. She helps her co-workers.

B Rita talks with a co-worker. Cross out the incorrect words. Then circle *True* or *False*.

1. Rita: Are you leaving?

Co-worker: Yes. It's time for me to go.

Rita: When **does / do** you finish work?

Co-worker: I work **from / on** 9 **to / from** 5. It's 5 o'clock.

Rita: But the manager **needs / need** these reports today.

Co-worker: Well, I have plans.

2. Rita's co-worker is a team player. True False

C Rita talks with a co-worker.

1. Co-worker: I can't do this. I **always / never** do it right.

Rita: What's wrong?

Co-worker: My timesheet **isn't / aren't** correct.

Rita: I can help you. **Always / Sometimes** put the days of the week here.

Co-worker: Oh, I see. I **usual / usually** make that mistake. Thank you, Rita.

Rita: You're welcome. I'm happy to help.

2. Rita is a team player. True False

D JOB INFORMATION. **Rita is an office assistant. She started this job right after high school. She has worked in the office for a few years. She knows many things about how the office works. Choose the correct answers.**

1. Rita can help train a new office assistant. True False

2. Rita had a few years of training before getting this job. True False

Lesson 1: Vocabulary

A What's for breakfast? Match the words with the pictures.

apples	bananas	bread	butter
cereal	eggs	oranges	~~yogurt~~

1. _yogurt_   2. _____   3. _____   4. _____

5. _____   6. _____   7. _____   8. _____

B Write the names of the foods.

1. _cabbage_   2. _____   3. _____   4. _____   5. _____

6. _____   7. _____   8. _____   9. _____   10. _____

C How often does Ada eat each kind of food? Complete the sentences.

	Never	Once a day	Twice a day	3-5 times a day
Grains		✓		
Vegetables			✓	
Fruit	✓			
Protein				✓
Dairy		✓		

1. Ada eats _____grains_____ once a day.

2. She eats _____ twice a day.

3. She never eats _____.

4. She eats _____ three to five times a day.

5. She has _____ once a day.

D How often do you eat these foods? Complete the chart.

	Never	Once a day	Twice a day	3-5 times a day
Grains				
Vegetables				
Fruit				
Protein				
Dairy				

E Look at the chart in Exercise D. Write sentences.

1. _I eat grains three times a day._

2. _____

3. _____

4. _____

5. _____

Lessons 2 & 3: Listening and Grammar

A Put the foods in the correct column.

~~apple~~	~~beef~~	butter	wrap	cereal	pasta
egg	lettuce	pancake	potato	taco	yogurt

Count			Non-count		
apple	_____	_____	_beef_	_____	_____
_____	_____	_____	_____	_____	_____

B Complete the sentences. Write the correct food and *it* or *them*.

1. I like ___bananas___.

I eat ___them___ every day.

2. I love ___steak___.

I eat ___it___ with onions.

3. I love _____.

I eat _____ for lunch every day.

4. I usually have _____ for breakfast.

I eat _____ before I go to work.

5. I eat _____ once a day.

I have _____ with dinner.

6. I usually have _____ for breakfast.

I eat _____ with cheese.

C Look at the pictures. Complete the conversations.

1. **A:** Do you like eggs?

   B: Not really. I like _pancakes_.

2. **A:** Do you want an apple?

   B: No, thanks. I don't really like _____.

3. **A:** Do you like bananas?

   B: Not really. I like _____.

4. **A:** Do you want a vegetable for dinner?

   B: Yes, I'd like _____.

5. **A:** Do you want fish for dinner?

   B: No, thanks. I don't really

   like _____.

6. **A:** What do you want for lunch?

   B: I want _____.

D Complete the conversation. Add *a* when necessary.

A: Wow, I'm really hungry.

B: Me, too. What do you want?

A: First I want (**hamburger**) ___*a hamburger*___.

B: First?

A: Yeah, then I want (**taco**) _____. I love _____.

B: I want _____, too.

A: Then I want (**pizza**) _____.

B: _____? What kind of _____ do you want?

A: Cheese. I want cheese _____. And I want a large iced tea.

Lesson 4: Reading

Ⓐ DEVELOP YOUR ACADEMIC SKILLS. Read the Academic Skill. Complete the sentences.

1. You should wash your hands for _____.
   a. 20 seconds   **b.** 20 minutes   **c.** 30 seconds

2. Pay attention to the _____ of your cutting boards.
   a. size   **b.** color   **c.** shape

> **Academic Skill: Read captions**
>
> The words you see above or below a picture are **captions**. They often add important information about the picture. Before you read an article, look at any pictures and read their captions.

Ⓑ ▶ Listen and read.

FOOD SAFETY

These safety steps can help you prevent food illnesses.

CLEAN
Keep your hands clean. Clean everything you use to cook food. First, wash your hands. Then wash where you prepare the food. This includes cutting boards, tables, and dishes.
5 Finally, wash all fruits and vegetables. Do not wash meat because the water might make the food dangerous.

SEPARATE
Keep meats, fish, and eggs separate from other foods like fruits and vegetables. Use separate cutting boards for meat and vegetables. Use red cutting boards for red meat. Use
10 yellow cutting boards for chicken. Separate these foods in the refrigerator, too. Use green for cutting fruits and vegetables.

COOK
Make sure food is the right temperature. Check the temperature carefully. It is dangerous to eat food that is not cooked enough. For example, it is dangerous to eat some
15 meats if you do not cook them enough.

CHILL
Put food away quickly. Put it in the refrigerator or freezer to be safe.

Wash your hands for 20 seconds.

Use different colored cutting boards for different foods.

Ⓒ CITE EVIDENCE. Complete the sentences. Where is the information? Write the line number.

Lines

1. Always wash _____ before cooking.
   a. meat   **b.** eggs   **c.** vegetables   _____

2. You should use a red cutting board for _____.
   a. chicken   **b.** red meat   **c.** vegetables   _____

3. It is dangerous to eat _____ that is not the right temperature.
   a. meat   **b.** fruit   **c.** vegetables   _____

4. Put food in the _____ after eating.
   a. stove   **b.** refrigerator   **c.** cabinet   _____

Lessons 5 & 6: Listening and Grammar

A Match the questions with the responses.

1. Would you like soup or salad?   _c_   a. Yes, an iced tea, please.

2. Would you like onion or tomato soup?   ___   b. Yes, please.

3. Would you like potatoes?   ___   ~~c.~~ Soup, please.

4. Fries or baked?   ___   d. Large, please.

5. Anything to drink?   ___   e. Baked, please.

6. Large or small?   ___   f. Tomato, please. And a turkey sandwich.

B ▶ Listen. Write the order.

Date				

Burger Heaven
Guest Check

	a green salad	

Lesson 7: Workplace, Life, and Community Skills

A Look at the supermarket ads. Complete the conversations.

Quick-Shop

Chicken ....$3.79/lb.

Potatoes ....99¢/lb.

Bread...........$3.89

Cheese ....$3.29/lb.

Steak ....$5.99/lb.

Apples ....79¢/lb.

Yogurt...........99¢

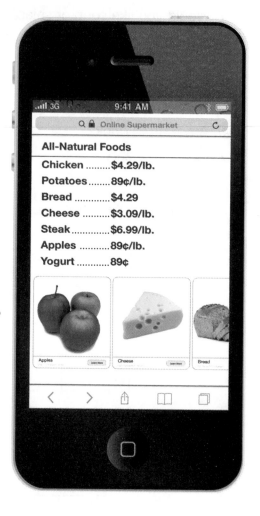

1. **A:** How much is the chicken at All-Natural Foods?

   B: It's ___$4.29 a pound___.

2. **A:** How much are the potatoes at Quick-Shop Foods?

   B: They're _____.

3. **A:** How much is the bread at All-Natural Foods?

   B: It's _____.

4. **A:** How much is the cheese at Quick-Shop Foods?

   B: It's _____.

5. **A:** How much is the steak at All-Natural Foods?

   B: It's _____.

6. **A:** How much are the apples at Quick-Shop Foods?

   B: They're _____.

7. **A:** How much is the yogurt at All-Natural Foods?

   B: It's _____.

B Look at the ads in Exercise A. Where is each food cheaper? Circle the cheaper price.

C ▶ Listen. Circle the letter of the correct answer.

1. Green beans are on sale for _____ a pound.

   a. $1.09   **b.** $1.19   **c.** $1.29

2. Potatoes are _____ a pound.

   a. 79¢   **b.** 69¢   **c.** 71¢

3. Fish is on sale for _____ a pound.

   a. $2.99   **b.** $3.99   **c.** $5.99

4. Chicken is _____ a pound.

   a. $4.99   **b.** $3.59   **c.** $4.59

5. Bread is on sale for _____.

   a. $2.99   **b.** $3.59   **c.** $2.49

D Look at the nutrition labels. Complete the sentences.

1. Cereal A has about ____10____ servings per container.

2. Cereal B has about _____ servings per container.

3. Cereal A has _____ calories per serving.

4. Cereal B has _____ calories per serving.

5. Cereal A has _____ of sodium.

6. Cereal B has _____ of sodium.

7. Cereal A has _____ of sugar.

8. Cereal B has _____ of sugar.

9. _____ has more sugar.

Nutrition	enter food name in All food categories Search

Cereal A

Nutrition Facts

Serving Size: 1.1 oz
Servings Per Container: About 10
Calories 120
Fat.. 0 g
Sodium ....150 mg
Sugar ....12 g

Nutrition	enter food name in All food categories Search

Cereal B

Nutrition Facts

Serving Size: 1.1 oz
Servings Per Container: About 9
Calories 110
Fat..0 g
Sodium .... 220 mg
Sugar ....24 g

E GO ONLINE. Now find similar information (calories, fat, sodium, and sugar) online about your favorite food.

Lessons 8 & 9: Listening and Grammar

A Complete the conversations. Use *how much / many*, *a lot*, or *not many / much*.

1. **A:** _____How much butter_____ is there?

   B: _____Not much_____. We need to buy more.

2. **A:** _____How many onions_____ do we have?

   B: _____Not many_____. We only have two. Let's get some more.

3. **A:** _____ is there?

   B: _____. We don't need to get more.

4. **A:** _____ is there?

   B: _____. We need to get more.

5. **A:** _____ is there?

   B: _____. We don't need to get more.

6. **A:** _____ do we have?

   B: _____. We have three large boxes!

7. **A:** _____ are there?

   B: _____. We only have two.

8. **A:** _____ do we have?

   B: _____. And they're big!

B Look at the recipe. Complete the conversation. Use *much* or *many*.

1. **A:** How _____*much turkey*_____ do we need?
   (turkey)

   B: We need ____*two pounds*____.

2. **A:** How _____?
   (rice)

   B: We need _____.

3. **A:** How _____?
   (peppers)

   B: We need _____.

4. **A:** How _____?
   (onions)

   B: We need _____.

5. **A:** How _____?
   (milk)

   B: We need _____.

6. **A:** How _____?
   (cheese)

   B: We need _____.

7. **A:** How _____?
   (vegetable oil)

   B: We need _____.

C

Turkey and Rice _____

Ingredients:
2 lbs. turkey
12 oz. rice
2 small peppers
3 small onions
8 oz. milk
10 oz. cheese
2 oz. vegetable oil

Print Recipe
★★★★★

C ▶ Listen. Paul and Marie are planning a party. Check (✓) the foods.

✓ grilled chicken	___ cake	___ fried chicken	___ fries
___ green salad	___ apple pie	___ juice	___ rice
___ soda	___ soup	___ tea	___ water

Lesson 10: Writing

A Read the Writing Skill. Rewrite the sentences.

1. I eat tacos for lunch.

    I have tacos for lunch.

2. He drinks juice every day.

    _____

3. I have a cup of coffee every morning.

    _____

4. She eats vegetables five times a week.

    _____

5. Ana has eggs for breakfast every day.

    _____

> **Writing Skill: Choose the correct verb**
> Use the verb *eat* when you talk about food. Use the verb *drink* when you talk about drinks. You can use *have* with food or drinks.
>
> For example:
> I (have) milk with my breakfast.
> I (drink) coffee with lunch.
> I (eat) pasta for dinner.

B Look at the pictures. Describe what Carl eats.

1.   **2.**   **3.**   **4.**   **5.**   **6.**   **7.**

Every morning Carl __drinks__ __coffee__. He usually _____ _____ for breakfast. For lunch, Carl usually _____ _____ _____ and _____. Carl sometimes _____ _____ for dinner. Once a week he goes to a restaurant for dinner. He usually _____ _____ _____ and _____.

C Read the text. Correct three errors with verbs.

In the morning, I usually has three eggs, cereal, and juice. For lunch, I usually eat tacos and pizza. I usually eat a large soda. For dinner, I eat chicken and rice. Sometimes I take ice cream at night. That's a lot of food!

Lesson 11: Soft Skills at Work

A TAKE ACTION. Cross out the incorrect words.

A person who takes action **makes / doesn't make** decisions on his or her own.

Nasir works at a restaurant. He's a dishwasher.

B Nasir speaks to a server. Cross out the incorrect information. Then circle *True* or *False*.

1. Server: It's so busy! We don't **have / has** any clean **glass / glasses**.

   Nasir: Oh, I see. These tables aren't clean. There is still **a rice / rice** on them.

   Server: Yes, I know. The other server is new. There are **many / much** glasses on the dirty tables.

   Nasir: Let me help you. We can bring the glasses into the kitchen. I'll wash them quickly.

2. Nasir takes action.   True   False

C Nasir speaks to the cook. Cross out the incorrect information. Then circle *True* or *False*.

1. Cook: Oh, no. The **tomatoes / tomatos** are bad! I can't use them.

   Nasir: Can I help? I can go to the farmer's market. How **many / much** tomatoes do you need?

   Cook: We need about 20 pounds.

   Nasir: That's no problem. Do you need any potatoes **and / or** onions?

   Cook: No, I have enough.

2. Nasir doesn't take action.   True   False

D JOB INFORMATION. **Nasir is a dishwasher at a restaurant. He also helps clean the restaurant. He works in the kitchen and sees many things. Choose the correct answers.**

1. Nasir knows where to find the dishes.   True   False

2. Nasir often talks to customers.   True   False

Unit 9: Rain or Shine

Lesson 1: Vocabulary

A Look at the thermometer. Label it with the words *cold*, *warm*, *hot*, and *cool*.

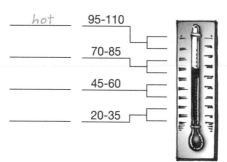

_____hot_____ 95-110

_____ 70-85

_____ 45-60

_____ 20-35

B Match the words with the pictures.

a.

b.

c.

d.

1. cloudy __c__

2. rainy ____

3. sunny ____

4. snowy ____

C Look at the pictures. Write sentences about each scene. Use the words in the box.

~~cloudy~~   cold   cool   hot   rainy   snowy   sunny   ~~warm~~

1. _It's warm and cloudy._   **2.** _____   **3.** _____   **4.** _____

D What is the weather like in your native country? Write sentences.

In my country, _____.

_____.

Lessons 2 & 3: Listening and Grammar

A Complete the sentences. Use the verbs in parentheses.

1. Kara ____*is not working*____ in her office today. She's at home.
   (not work)

2. Carl and Martha _____ their daughter at college.
   (visit)

3. Bruno _____ on the sofa. He's in the bedroom now.
   (not sleep)

4. Steven _____ in the library.
   (study)

5. Roman and Cara _____ lunch. They're in a meeting now.
   (not eat)

6. Kate and Rob _____ dinner for us.
   (make)

B Unscramble the words to form sentences. Use contractions.

1. *She's talking on the phone.* _____
   (she / phone / talking / on / is / the)

2. _____
   (are / we / TV / watching)

3. _____
   (am / reading / a / I / book)

4. _____
   (raining / is / Chicago / it / in)

5. _____
   (is / he / his / riding / bike)

6. _____
   (they / the / running / park / in / are)

7. _____
   (is / she / wearing / jacket / new / a)

8. _____
   (visiting / we / in / are / friends / Miami / our)

C Look at the picture. Complete the sentences with *'s, isn't, 're,* or *aren't,* and the verbs in parentheses.

1. She ___'s talking___ on the phone.
   (talk)

2. She _____ water.
   (drink)

3. She _____.
   (eat)

4. She _____ her homework.
   (do)

5. He _____ to music.
   (listen)

6. He _____ his homework.
   (do)

7. He _____ water.
   (drink)

8. He _____ on the phone.
   (talk)

9. They _____ in the kitchen.
   (sit)

10. They _____.
    (watch TV)

D Look at the picture. Describe what you see. Use the verbs in the box.

~~clean~~	cook	listen to music	read	sleep

1. ___He's cleaning the floor.___

2. _____

3. _____

4. _____

5. _____

Lesson 4: Workplace, Life, and Community Skills

A Match the advice with the emergencies.

a. an earthquake

b. a tornado

c. a landslide

d. a hurricane

e. a flood

f. a wildfire

1. Stay in the house. ___d___

3. Leave your home. _____

5. Avoid the smoke. _____

2. Go downstairs. _____

4. Go under a piece of furniture, like a desk. _____

6. Don't go swimming. _____

B Which type of bad weather do you have in your native country?

In my country, _____.

_____.

_____.

C Look at the floor plan of an office building. Complete the sentences in the notice.
Cross out the incorrect words.

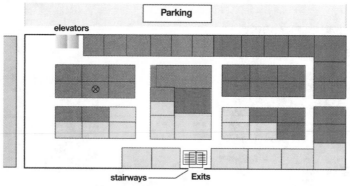

Notice:

There will be a fire drill at 10:00 a.m. today.

Please follow the safety rules.

1. You are in the office marked "X."
   During the drill, go to the **exit / ~~entrance~~**.
2. Do not use the **elevators / stairways**.
3. Exit the **building / elevator** quickly.
4. Go outside. Wait in the parking **lot / office**.

D Look at this storm preparation sheet.
Complete the sentences.

1. To prepare for a storm you need enough
   food and _____ for a week.

2. You should make sure that you have
   enough _____ to pay for things.

3. You should charge your _____
   and put gas in your _____.

E Prepare for storms in your area.
Add contact information to your phone for three emergency services that you might need if there is a storm. Include the name, phone number, address, and website.

Name	Phone number	Address	Website
_____	_____	_____	_____
_____	_____	_____	_____
_____	_____	_____	_____

Lessons 5 & 6: Listening and Grammar

A Look at the pictures. Answer the questions. Use short answers.

1.

    a. Is Sara reading a book?   <u>No, she isn't.</u>

    b. Is she talking on the phone?   _____

    c. Is she working?   _____

2.

    a. Is Sam working?   _____

    b. Is he running?   _____

    c. Is he listening to music?   _____

3.

    a. Are they eating?   _____

    b. Are they working?   _____

    c. Is it raining?   _____

B Complete the conversations. Use short answers.

1. **A:** __Is__ she _studying English_ ?
   (study English)
   B: No, _she isn't_ .

2. **A:** _____ you _____?
   (listen to music)
   B: No, _____.

3. **A:** _____ you _____?
   (shop for food)
   B: No, _____.

4. **A:** _____ it _____ in Seattle?
   (rain)
   B: Yes, _____.

5. **A:** _____ they _____ today?
   (go home)
   B: No, _____.

6. **A:** _____ it _____ in Denver?
   (snow)
   B: No, _____.

C Complete the conversation. Use the sentences in the box.

Great. Get matches, too.	~~No, I'm not. I'm reading a magazine.~~
Oh, good. Are you getting water?	Really?
Yes. We need good weather!	

Ann: Are you watching the news?

Tim: _No, I'm not. I'm reading a magazine._

Ann: Well, turn on the TV. A big storm is coming.

Tim: _____

Ann: Yes. In fact, I'm coming home early. I'm at the grocery store now.

Tim: _____

Ann: Yes. I'm getting water, food, and a lot of batteries.

Tim: _____

Ann: OK. Do we need anything else?

Tim: _____

D ▶ Listen. Check your answers to Exercise C.

Lesson 7: Reading

A Listen and read.

FACTS ABOUT TORNADOES

National Centers for Environmental Information

What is a tornado? A tornado is a storm with very strong wind. The wind moves in a circle. Sometimes it looks like a cone. The top is bigger than the bottom. A tornado can touch the ground. This makes it very dangerous. It can do
5 a lot of damage.

In the U.S., about 1,200 tornadoes happen every year. They happen most often in the central part of the U.S. This is sometimes called "Tornado Alley." However, tornadoes can happen in other states, too.

10 Most tornadoes happen during May, June, and July. They can also happen during other months. They happen most often between 4:00 and 9:00 p.m.

It is important to know the safety rules. When there is a tornado warning, you need to follow the rules. If you are in your home, go to the lowest floor like a basement. Stay away from windows.

B DEVELOP YOUR ACADEMIC SKILLS. Read the article again. Answer the questions.

1. When do most tornadoes take place?
   a. winter   **b.** summer   **c.** spring and summer

2. Where do tornadoes occur in the U.S.?
   a. the north   **b.** the southeast   **c.** the central part

> **Academic Skill: Focus on details**
>
> The first time you read an article, read for the main idea. Then read again and focus on details. The details answer the questions *who*, *what*, *when*, *where*, *how*, and *why*.

C CITE EVIDENCE. Complete the sentences. Where is the information? Write the line number.

Lines

1. A tornado is dangerous because it has _____.
   a. very heavy rain   **b.** very strong wind   **c.** a storm surge   _____

2. Sometimes tornadoes look like _____.
   a. a triangle   **b.** a circle   **c.** a cone   _____

3. There are about _____ tornadoes each year in the U.S.
   a. 2,000   **b.** 12,000   **c.** 1,200   _____

D INTERPRET. Look at the map. Complete the sentences.

1. _____ is one of the states at the south of Tornado Alley.
   a. Indiana   **b.** Texas   **c.** Nebraska

2. _____ is one of the states at the north of Tornado Alley.
   a. Ohio   **b.** Arkansas   **c.** North Dakota

Lessons 8 & 9: Listening and Grammar

A Look at the pictures. Complete the sentences. Use *a* or *an* when necessary.

1. It's very cold out. You need _____ *earmuffs* _____ and _____ *gloves* _____.

2. I need _____. It's really sunny out today.

3. It's pretty cold and rainy out. Do you have _____ and _____?

4. You need _____ when you're running. It's very sunny.

5. It's pretty cold and it's snowing. You need _____ and _____.

B Unscramble the words to form sentences.

1. _____.
   (really / hot / in / it's / and / Dallas / today / humid)

2. _____.
   (it's / cold / and / in / pretty / snowing / Boston / now)

3. _____.
   (foggy / in / San Francisco / it's / very / winter / the / in)

4. _____.
   (spring / weather / pretty / in / the / in / New York / nice / is / the)

C ▶ Listen to the weather reports. Circle the letter of the correct answer.

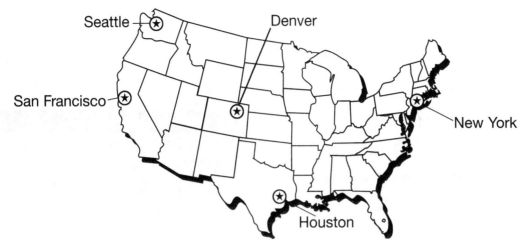

1. The weather in San Francisco is _____.

   a. cold and very foggy

   b. cool and very foggy

   c. cool but not foggy

2. The weather in Seattle is _____.

   a. rainy and pretty cool

   b. rainy and pretty cold

   c. rainy and pretty warm

3. In New York, it's _____.

   a. sunny and pretty hot

   b. sunny and pretty warm

   c. sunny and very hot

4. The weather in Houston today is _____.

   a. really humid

   b. really cool

   c. really warm

5. In Denver, it's _____.

   a. not very cold

   b. very cold

   c. very cool

Lesson 10: Writing

A Read the Writing Skill. Complete the sentences. Use words from the box.

> I work outside   I love the cold weather   it's very cold
>
> ~~it's warm, but not hot~~   I like to swim

1. My favorite month is May because

it's warm, but not hot .

> **Writing Skill: Use *because* to give a reason**
> The word *because* gives a reason. It explains why. For example:
> Why does he like hot weather? He likes hot weather (because) he loves the beach.

2. My favorite season is winter because

_____.

3. I don't like winter because

_____.

4. I like the hot weather because

_____.

5. I like sunny, warm weather because

_____.

B Look at the picture. Combine sentences using *because*.

1. I love Boston. The winter there is beautiful.

I love Boston because the winter there is beautiful.

2. I like the snow. Winter is my favorite season.

_____

3. I always wear gloves in the winter. My hands get very cold.

_____

C Read the text. Correct three errors.

I love San Francisco. It's my favorite city because I don't love the weather there. In the summer, it warm. It's not very hot. Fall is my favorite season because it is usually warm and sunny. In the winter, it is sometimes rainy. In the spring, it very cool.

Lesson 11: Soft Skills at Work

A LEARN NEW SKILLS. How can you be ready to learn new skills? Check (✓) the correct answers.

❑ **a.** want to learn

❑ **b.** be excited about learning

❑ **c.** repeat old ideas

❑ **d.** read about new ideas

❑ **e.** attend trainings

Yefim is a teacher. He learns new things in his job.

B Yefim talks to a teacher. Complete the conversation. Cross out the incorrect words. Then circle *True* or *False*.

1. Co-worker: We have a new app for taking attendance. I **am / are** using it. It's great!

Yefim: Is **it / they** easy to use?

Co-worker: Yes, it's **really / never** easy. I can show you.

Yefim: That's **pretty / nice** good! You know I don't like new technology.

Co-worker: It's not very difficult.

Yefim: That sounds good. I **is / am** going to try it.

2. Yesim is ready to learn new skills.   True   False

C Yefim talks to another teacher. Complete the conversation. Cross out the incorrect words. Then circle *True* or *False*.

1. Co-worker: We're **having / have** another meeting about the new computers.

Yefim: That's a **very / much** good idea, isn't it?

Co-worker: I don't think so.

Yefim: Why not?

Co-worker: I **really / pretty** don't want to go. I know how to use a computer.

We don't **need / needing** more meetings.

Yefim: Well, you might learn something new at the meeting

2. Yefim's co-worker is not ready to learn new skills.   True   False

D JOB INFORMATION. Yefim is a teacher. Look at the job information. Choose the correct answer.

Work Environment	Schools, colleges, training centers
Work Experience	Student teaching
Education	College degree

1. Yefim can work in different places.   True   False

2. Yefim never has to learn new things.   True   False

Lesson 1: Vocabulary

A Look at the map of Watertown. Write the places.

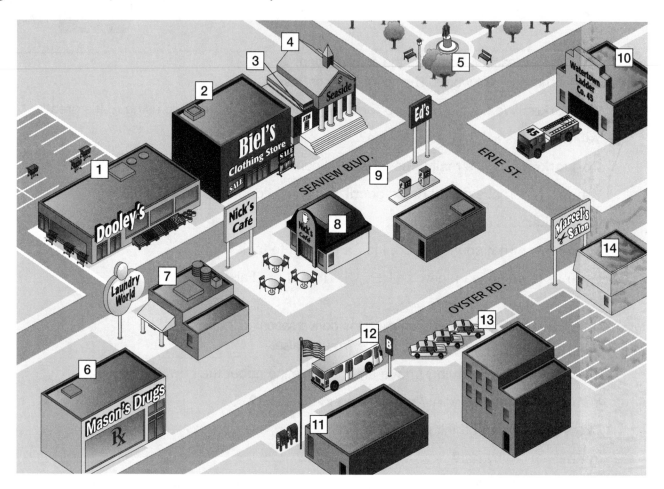

1. ___a supermarket___

2. _____

3. _____

4. _____

5. _____

6. _____

7. _____

8. _____

9. _____

10. _____

11. _____

12. _____

13. _____

14. _____

B Look at the map in Exercise A. Complete the conversations.

1. **A:** Is there a bank in Watertown?

    B: Yes, there is. There's a bank _____ on Seaview Boulevard _____.

2. **A:** Is there a post office in Watertown?

    B: Yes, there is. There's a post office _____.

3. **A:** Is there a supermarket in Watertown?

    B: Yes, there is. There's a supermarket _____.

4. **A:** Is there a drugstore in Watertown?

    B: Yes, there is. There's a drugstore _____.

5. **A:** Is there a fire station in Watertown?

    B: Yes, there is. There's a fire station _____.

6. **A:** Is there a salon in Watertown?

    B: Yes, there is. There's a salon _____.

7. **A:** Is there a laundromat in Watertown?

    B: Yes, there is. There's a laundromat _____.

8. **A:** Is there a park in Watertown?

    B: Yes, there is. There's a park _____.

C Match the sentences with the correct places.

1. Ramon is running.	c	**a.**	the post office
2. Laura is getting money.	___	**b.**	the drugstore
3. Mr. Lopez is picking up a package.	___	**c.**	the park
4. Mrs. Smith is having a cup of coffee.	___	**d.**	the supermarket
5. Carlos is buying apples.	___	**e.**	the bank
6. Maya is getting medicine.	___	**f.**	the café

Lessons 2 & 3: Listening and Grammar

A Look at the map. Complete the sentences. Cross out the incorrect words.

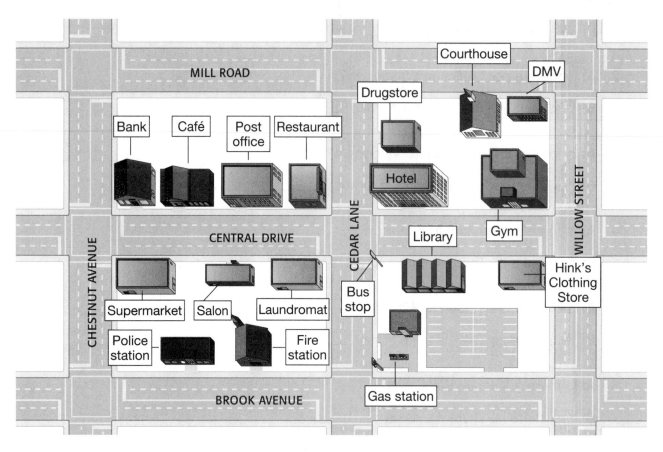

1. The post office is **on /** ~~near~~ Central Drive **between /** ~~next to~~ Chestnut Avenue and Cedar Lane.

2. The courthouse is **on / near** Mill Road **between / next to** the DMV.

3. The bank is **across from / next to** the café.

4. The gym is **across from / next to** Hink's Clothing Store.

5. The gas station is **on the corner of / near** Cedar Lane and Brook Avenue.

6. The supermarket is **down / on** the block from the laundromat.

7. The police station is **across from / next to** the fire station.

8. The drugstore is **around the corner / across** from the hotel.

B Look at the map in Exercise A. Complete the sentences. Use the prepositions in the box. Some prepositions are used more than once.

around the corner from	between	down the block from	near	on the corner of

1. Hink's Clothing Store is _____*on the corner of*_____ Central Drive and Willow Street.

2. The post office is _____ the bank.

3. The hotel is _____ Cedar Lane and Willow Street.

4. The supermarket is _____ from the laundromat.

5. The bus stop is _____ the library.

6. The DMV is _____ Willow Street and Mill Road.

7. The drugstore is _____ from the hotel.

8. The restaurant is _____ from the bank.

9. The courthouse is _____ from the drugstore.

10. The police station is _____ Chestnut Avenue and Cedar Lane.

C Look at the map in Exercise A. Read the descriptions of where the places are located. Write the names of the places.

1. It's on Central Drive between Cedar Lane and Chestnut Avenue.

   It's between the bank and the post office. What is it?

   _____*the café*_____

2. It's across from Hink's Clothing Store on the corner of Willow Street. What is it?

   _____

3. It's near the laundromat and next to the salon. What is it?

   _____

Lesson 4: Workplace, Life, and Community Skills

A Look at the pictures. Complete the conversations.

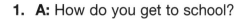

1. **A:** How do you get to school?

   B: _I drive._____

2. **A:** How does Monika get to school?

   B: _____

3. **A:** How do your children get to school?

   B: _____

4. **A:** How does Mrs. Martin get to school?

   B: _____

5. **A:** How does your brother get to work?

   B: _____

6. **A:** How do your parents get to work?

   B: _____

B Look at the bus schedules. Complete the sentences.

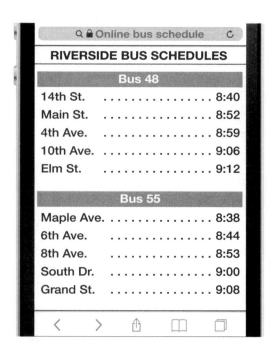

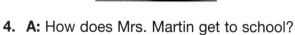

1. Bus 48 leaves 14th Street at ___8:40___.
2. Bus 55 leaves _Maple Avenue_ at 8:38.
3. Bus 48 leaves Main Street at _____.
4. Bus 55 leaves 6th Avenue at _____.
5. Bus 48 leaves _____ at 8:59
6. Bus 55 leaves 8th Avenue at _____.
7. Bus 48 leaves 10th Avenue at _____.
8. Bus 55 leaves _____ at 9:00.
9. Bus 48 leaves _____ at 9:12.
10. Bus 55 leaves Grand Street at _____.

Q 🔒 Online bus schedule ↻

RIVERSIDE BUS SCHEDULES

Bus 48	
14th St.	8:40
Main St.	8:52
4th Ave.	8:59
10th Ave.	9:06
Elm St.	9:12

Bus 55	
Maple Ave.	8:38
6th Ave.	8:44
8th Ave.	8:53
South Dr.	9:00
Grand St.	9:08

< > ⬆ 📖 🗔

Lessons 5 & 6: Listening and Grammar

A Complete the conversation. Use the questions in the box.

How do you get to the high school?	How much does the train cost?
Where do you buy a ticket?	Where do you get the train?

Meg: _How do you get to the high school?_

Rob: Take the Number 12 train.

Meg: OK. _____

Rob: Around the corner on Colombo Road.

Meg: Great. _____

Rob: In the station.

Meg: Thanks. One more question. _____

Rob: $2.50.

B ▶ Listen. Check your answers to Exercise A.

C Complete the conversation. Use the questions in the box.

How much does the bus cost?	What time does the bus leave the station?
Where do you get off?	Which bus goes to the high school?

Mark: _Which bus goes to the high school?_

Lisa: The Number 27 bus goes to the high school.

Mark: OK. _____

Lisa: At 7:15.

Mark: _____

Lisa: $3.50.

Mark: Thanks. One more question. _____

Lisa: Dupont Square.

D ▶ Listen. Check your answers to Exercise C.

E Complete the conversation. Make questions in the simple present with *how, how much,* or *where.*

A: _____How do_____ you get to Watertown High School?

B: Take the Number 8 bus.

A: _____ you get it?

B: At Crawford Street.

A: _____ it cost?

B: $3.50.

A: _____ you get off?

B: At Newport Avenue.

F Unscramble the words to make questions. Use *do* or *does* and the words in parentheses.

1. _How do you get to Nick's Café?_
   (how / get / you / Nick's Café)

2. _____
   (how much / cost / the train)

3. _____
   (where / get off / you)

4. _____
   (where / the Number 6 bus / you / get)

5. _____
   (how much / cost / the bus)

6. _____
   (how / get / the library / you)

7. _____
   (where / you / a ticket / the bus / for / buy)

8. _____
   (how / you / the train station / get to)

Lesson 7: Reading

A Listen and read.

THE U.S. POST OFFICE

The United States Post Office is an organization that delivers mail. There are more than 30,000 post offices in the United States. More than 7 million people work in the postal service.

Post offices provide many mailing services. You can mail letters and
5 packages. You can also get your own PO Box (post office box). This means people can send mail to your box at the post office. The post office can also help you if you move homes. They can forward your mail. This means they automatically deliver it to your new address.

You can do other kinds of things at the post office, too. For example,
10 you can get a money order. This is a check that you can use to pay someone. You can also apply for a passport. The workers at the post office can take your passport picture. They can also help you with the application.

The post office offers a lot more than stamps.

You can send packages at the post office

B DEVELOP YOUR ACADEMIC SKILLS. Read the Academic Skill. Write down one example of post office services from the reading.

_____

_____

_____

Academic Skill: Give your own examples

Writers often give examples to help the reader understand their ideas. Try to think of examples of your own when you read.

C CITE EVIDENCE. Complete the sentences. Where is the information? Write the line number.

Lines

1. There are more than _____ post offices in the U.S.
   a. 30,000   **b.** 29,000   **c.** 31,000   ____

2. You can mail letters and _____ in the post office.
   a. stamps   **b.** checks   **c.** packages   ____

3. You can get your own _____ at the post office.
   a. PO box   **b.** package   **c.** checks   ____

4. If you want a passport, the post office can _____.
   a. give you one   **b.** send it for you   **c.** take your picture   ____

Lessons 8 & 9: Listening and Grammar

A Complete the conversation. Use the present continuous tense and the verbs in parentheses. Use contractions when possible.

A: What **(do)** ___are___ you ___doing___ on Saturday?

B: I **(go)** _____ to a party.

A: Who **(go)** _____ you _____ with?

B: My sister **(go)** _____ with me.

A: How **(get)** _____ you _____ there?

B: We **(drive)** _____ .

B Look at the pictures. Complete the conversations.

1. **A:** What __is__ Michael doing this weekend?

   B: ___He's going to a concert___ on Sunday.

2. **A:** What ____ you doing this weekend?

   B: _____ on Saturday.

3. **A:** What ____ your sisters doing this weekend?

   B: _____

4. **A:** What ____ Mika doing this weekend?

   B: _____

5. **A:** What _____ Mr. Ray doing this weekend?

   B: _____

C Unscramble the words to form questions.

1. _Where is he going this weekend?_
   (he / where / this / going / weekend / is)

2. _____
   (you / what / on / are / Saturday / doing / night)

3. _____
   (going / who / with / to / you / are / movies / the)

4. _____
   (getting / concert / to / how / sister / your / the / is)

5. _____
   (you / who / playing / with / are / soccer / Sunday / on)

6. _____
   (they / what / doing / Friday / are / night / on)

D ▶ Listen. Complete the advertisements.

Lesson 10: Writing

A Read the Writing Skill. Circle the prepositions in the sentences.

1. I live (on) Broadway.

2. The café is next to the library.

3. The bus stop is down the block.

4. The supermarket is around the corner from my house.

5. The drugstore is between the police station and the salon.

> **Writing Skill: Use prepositions**
>
> Prepositions are very different in every language. Be sure you use the correct preposition in English. For example: The Post Office is (on) Main Street.

B Look at the picture. Complete the paragraph.

on	~~down~~
next to	around the corner

My street

I live at 28 Maple Street. I take the bus to work. The bus stop is _____ *down* _____ the block. There's a café _____ Lakeview Road. _____ the café is a gym. The library is _____ from the café. I like my street because everything is close by.

C Read the text. Correct four errors with prepositions.

I live in Elm Street. There are a lot of stores near my home. There is a supermarket on the block from my house. There's a café in the corner and a salon across the street. And a drugstore is around the street from my house.

A BE RELIABLE. Look at the words. Which ones describe a person who is reliable?

Lesson 11: Soft Skills at Work

Check (✓) the correct answers.

- ❑ **a.** is always at work on time
- ❑ **b.** comes to work late
- ❑ **c.** calls a supervisor when late
- ❑ **d.** doesn't always finish the work
- ❑ **e.** stays late to finish work, if necessary

Ani works at a hospital. She's a nurse's assistant.

B Ani talks to a nurse at work. Cross out the incorrect words. Then circle *True* or *False*.

1. Nurse: Ani, I have an emergency **between / down** the hall. I have to leave.

Ani: **How / What** can I help?

Nurse: When **do you start / you end** your shift?

Ani: I'm **start / starting** at 4:00.

Nurse: Can you help with Mrs. King? I'm **giving / give** her breakfast.

Ani: Of course.

Nurse: Thank you, Ani.

2. Ani is reliable.   True   False

C Ani talks to a co-worker at work. Cross out the incorrect words. Then circle *True* or *False*.

1. Ani: Carla. The supervisor **is looking / look** for you.

Co-worker: Sorry I'm late. The traffic was **really / not** bad.

Ani: **Where / How much** was it bad?

Co-worker: It was bad **between / over** George Street and Purple Lane.

Ani: I'm **going / go** to let the supervisor know you're here. You should call.

Co-worker: Oh, well. I don't think it's important to call.

2. Ani's co-worker is reliable.   True   False

D JOB INFORMATION. Ani is a nurse's assistant. She helps care for patients. She helps them eat and get dressed. Sometimes she measures blood pressure and temperature. Choose the correct answers.

1. Ani talks to patients every day.   True   False

2. Ani's work is not important to the registered nurses.   True   False

Unit 11: Health Matters

Lesson 1: Vocabulary

A Look at the picture. Write the words.

1. _____head_____
2. _____
3. _____
4. _____
5. _____
6. _____
7. _____

8. _____
9. _____
10. _____
11. _____
12. _____
13. _____
14. _____

15. _____
16. _____
17. _____
18. _____
19. _____
20. _____

B Look at the words in the box. Put them in the correct column.

ankle	ears	eyes	elbow	foot
hand	knee	mouth	nose	wrist

Parts of the head

_____ears_____

_____

_____

_____

Parts of the arm

_____

_____

_____

Parts of the leg

_____

_____

_____

C Look at the pictures. Complete the sentences.

1. Touch your _____.

2. Shake your _____.

3. Nod your _____.

4. Clap your _____.

5. Touch your _____.

6. Shake your _____.

Lessons 2 & 3: Listening and Grammar

A Complete the conversation. Use the correct form of *feel*, *have*, or *hurt*.

A: How _____do_____ you _____feel_____?

B: I _____ terrible.

A: _____ you _____ a headache?

B: No. I _____ a headache. My stomach _____.

B Complete the sentences. Use the words in the box.

an earache	~~the flu~~	a headache	a stomachache

1. Martin: I can't go to work today. I think I have _____the flu_____.

2. Mrs. Ramirez: Jimmy can't go to school today. He has _____.

3. Mrs. Yu: I'm calling about my daughter. She's sick. She has _____.

4. Mr. Thompson: I'm calling about my son. He's sick. He has _____.

C Look at the pictures. Complete the sentences. Use the correct form of *feel*, *have*, or *hurt*.

1. Harry _____*has*_____ a headache.

He __*doesn't have*__ a fever.

2. My children _____ well.

They _____ stomachaches.

3. Robert _____ a bad toothache.

His tooth really _____.

4. Jill _____ well.

Her head _____.

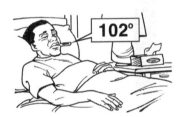

5. Hassan _____ sick.

He _____ a fever.

6. I _____ well.

I think I _____ the flu.

D Complete the conversation about Ericka. Use the words in parentheses.

A: _How does Ericka feel?_____ (how / Ericka / feel)

B: _____ (head / hurt)

A: _____ (have / fever)

B: _____ (no / have / fever)

A: _____ (have / stuffy nose)

B: _____ (yes / have / stuffy nose)

Lesson 4: Workplace, Life, and Community Skills

A ▶ Listen. Complete the text message.

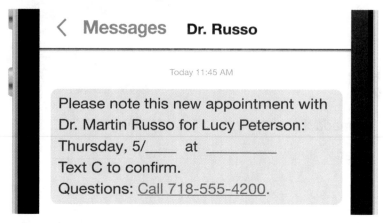

< **Messages** **Dr. Russo**

Today 11:45 AM

Please note this new appointment with
Dr. Martin Russo for Lucy Peterson:
Thursday, 5/_____ at _____
Text C to confirm.
Questions: Call 718-555-4200.

B Look at the text message. Complete the conversation.

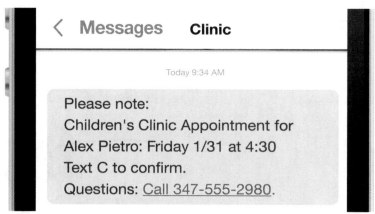

< **Messages** **Clinic**

Today 9:34 AM

Please note:
Children's Clinic Appointment for
Alex Pietro: Friday 1/31 at 4:30
Text C to confirm.
Questions: Call 347-555-2980.

Assistant: Children's Clinic. Can I help you?

Mrs. Pietro: This is Mrs. Pietro. I'd like to make an appointment for my son.

Assistant: Sure. What is your son's name?

Mrs. Pietro: His name is ___Alex___.

Assistant: Can he come in on Thursday?

Mrs. Pietro: No, I'm sorry.

Assistant: How about _____?

Mrs. Pietro: Yes, that's good.

Assistant: Is _____ OK?

Mrs. Pietro: Yes, we can be there.

Assistant: OK, that's _____, _____ at _____. I'll send a message to confirm.
See you then.

C Complete the doctor's sentences. Use the words in the box.

lie down	open	roll up	say	sit	~~step~~	take

1. OK, Tommy, please _____step_____ on the scale.

2. Now please _____ on the table.

3. OK. Now _____ your sleeve.

4. Let's see your throat. _____ your mouth and _____ "ahh."

5. And now let's check your chest. Please _____ a deep breath.

6. Now, please _____, Tommy. I'm going to check your stomach.

D Look at the medicine label. Complete the conversations.

ACETAFIL EXTRA
Pain Reliever

500 mg tablets
For relief of pain from
headaches, backaches,
toothaches, colds, fever

Directions:
Adults and Children 12 and older:
Take 2 tablets every 6 hours.

- **DO NOT TAKE MORE THAN 8 TABLETS A DAY.**
- **DO NOT OPERATE MACHINERY.**

ACETAFIL
Pain Reliever

250 mg tablets
For relief of pain from
headaches, backaches,
toothaches, colds, fever

Directions:
Adults and Children 12 and older:
Take 1 tablet every 4 hours.

- **DO NOT TAKE MORE THAN 4 TABLETS A DAY.**
- **DO NOT OPERATE MACHINERY.**

1. **A:** How often do I take this?

   B: Every _6 hours_____.

   A: How much do I take?

   B: You take _____.

   A: Can my son take this medicine?

   B: How old is he?

   A: He's 2.

   B: _____.

2. **A:** How often do I take this?

   B: Every _____.

   A: How much do I take?

   B: You take _____.

   A: Can my daughter take this medicine?

   B: How old is he?

   A: She's 12.

   B: _____.

Lessons 5 & 6: Listening and Grammar

A ▶ Listen. Complete the sentences with *was, wasn't, were,* or *weren't*.

1. I ___was___ sick yesterday. I ___wasn't___ at work.

2. Carlos _____ at home last night. He _____ at his cousin's house.

3. Marie _____ absent last night. She _____ in class.

4. We _____ sick last week. We _____ in school.

5. They _____ in class yesterday. They _____ sick.

B Look at the attendance chart. Today is Thursday. Find the people and complete the sentences.

Attendance Chart

Name	Mon.	Tues.	Wed.	Thurs.	Fri.
Hung	✓	✓	A	✓	
Dominik	✓	A	✓	✓	
Ria	✓	A	✓	✓	
Yoko	✓	✓	A	✓	
Carolina	A	A	A	✓	

1. ___Hung___ wasn't in class yesterday. She ___was___ here on Monday and Tuesday.

2. _____ and _____ were here yesterday, but they _____ here on Tuesday.

3. _____ was absent yesterday. She was here on Monday and Tuesday.

4. _____ was sick this week. She _____ in school Monday, Tuesday, or Wednesday.

5. _____ wasn't here Tuesday, but she _____ here today.

C Read the e-mail. Complete the sentences. Use *was, were, wasn't,* or *weren't*.

I ___was___ in New York last night. I _____ at a party. It _____ a surprise party for my parents. The problem _____ that my parents _____ there. They _____ both at home. My parents _____ both sick. The surprise was on us! It _____ much fun without my parents.

Lesson 7: Reading

A Listen and read.

WAYS TO STAY HEALTHY

There are many kinds of exercise for good health. Some exercise helps you to relax, like yoga.

Other activities, like running and walking, help your heart. Swimming is another great exercise. It helps your entire body. Riding a bike is good for your health, and it's fun. If you go to a gym, you can do exercises, like lifting weights, to make your body strong.

5 The U.S. Department of Health and Human Services says you will live longer if you exercise. They have guidelines about how much exercise you need. For example, they say to exercise three to five times a week. You will add 3.5 years to your life if you do everything they say 100%. Choose an activity you enjoy, and you will have more energy, and your body will be stronger. You will also have a healthier life and live longer!

B DEVELOP YOUR ACADEMIC SKILLS. **Read the Academic Skill. Answer the questions.**

1. Is it useful to learn that you can live longer?

   ❏ Yes   ❏ No

2. Thinking about how much exercise you get is a way to apply what you read.

   ❏ Yes   ❏ No

> **Academic Skill: Apply what you read**
>
> Use what you learn from the reading to think about the world. Does the information change your ideas? Can it be useful to you, your family, or your friends?

C CITE EVIDENCE. **Complete the sentences. Where is the information? Write the line number.**

Lines

1. Running and _____ help your heart.
   a. sitting   **b.** lifting weights   **c.** walking   _____

2. One exercise that can help you to relax is _____.
   a. lifting weights   **b.** running   **c.** yoga   _____

3. You should exercise _____ to stay healthy.
   a. 5 – 6 times a week   **b.** 3 – 5 times a week   **c.** 3 – 5 times a day   _____

4. According to the U.S. Department of Health and Human Services, you can add _____ years to your life if you follow the guidelines 100%.
   a. 2.5   **b.** 3.5   **c.** 5.5   _____

Lessons 8 & 9: Listening and Grammar

A ▶ Listen to the conversations. Write *should* or *shouldn't*.

1. You ___should___ drink water.

2. He _____ go to school today.

3. You _____ drink a lot of juice.

4. She _____ go running.

5. She _____ drink tea and honey.

6. He _____ go to work.

B Complete the phone conversation. Use the sentences in the box.

Do you have a fever?	~~How are you? Is something wrong?~~
Oh, I'm sorry to hear that. What do you have?	You really shouldn't wait too long.
You should rest and drink a lot.	

Sara: Hi, Joe. This is Sara.

Joe: Hi, Sara. *How are you? Is something wrong?* _____

Sara: Well, I'm sick. I'm not coming to work today.

Joe: _____

Sara: I'm not sure. I have a headache, and my stomach doesn't feel good.

Joe: _____

Sara: Yes, I do. I just feel terrible.

Joe: Well, take it easy, Sara. _____

Sara: That's a good idea.

Joe: But call the doctor if you don't feel better soon.

_____

Sara: OK. Thanks Joe.

C ▶ Listen. Check your answers to Exercise B.

D Look at the pictures. Complete the conversations. Use *should* or *shouldn't* and one of the phrases in the box.

drink milk or juice	eat a piece of onion	put butter on it
take a hot shower	take antibiotics	~~use a heating pad~~

1.

A: I have a backache.

B: I'm sorry to hear that. _You should use a heating pad._

2.

A: I have bad cold.

B: I'm sorry to hear that. You _____.

3.

A: I have the flu.

B: You should rest. You _____.

4.

A: My tooth hurts.

B: I'm sorry to hear that. You _____.

5.

A: I have a bad burn.

B: You _____. You should put water on it.

6.

A: I have a stomachache.

B: You _____.

Lesson 10: Writing

A Read the Writing Skill. Then check (✓) the sentences that are good topic sentences.

❑ **1.** My sister has very good eating habits.

❑ **2.** Also, I drink tea when I'm sick.

❑ **3.** Fruits and vegetables are good for your health.

❑ **4.** Another example is running.

❑ **5.** She plays soccer once a week.

> **Writing Skill: Use a topic sentence**
>
> Start each paragraph with a topic sentence. A topic sentence tells the main idea of the paragraph.
>
> <u>I have many healthy habits.</u> I eat fruit and vegetables every day. I get exercise four times a week. I also get eight hours of sleep each night.

B Read the paragraph. Choose a topic sentence for the paragraph. Write it on the line.

My mother doesn't like hamburgers.

My mother has good habits for her health.

My mother enjoys running.

My mother loves watching TV.

_____

First, she eats healthy food. She eats a lot of fruits and vegetables. She doesn't eat fried food. Next, she runs or rides her bike four times a week. She also gets a lot of sleep each night. She has one bad habit. She watches TV every night. She should read a book.

C Read the text. Correct four errors with verb.

I have healthy and unhealthy habits. I love to eat fruit. I don't likes vegetables that much. I always eat a good breakfast. I don't eat a healthy lunch. I sometimes just has a soda. I go to the doctor for a check-up once a year. I gets exercise 2 times a week. I should exercise 4 or 5 times a week. I get 7 hours of sleep a night. I should 8 hours.

Lesson 11: Soft Skills at Work

A MAKE GOOD DECISIONS. How can you make good decisions at work? Check (✓) all that apply.

❑ **a.** think about health of others

❑ **b.** don't think about safety of others

❑ **c.** ask others to solve problems

❑ **d.** ask people to work when they're sick

Aya is an office assistant. She works Monday to Friday, 8:00 A.M. to 5:00 P.M.

B Aya talks to her supervisor. Complete the conversation.
Cross out the incorrect information. Then circle *True* or *False*.

1. Supervisor: Aya, why didn't you finish the report?

Aya: I'm sorry, Ms. Smith. I'm not **feeling / feel** well.

Supervisor: Okay, Aya. I'm sorry that you're not feeling well. **How / What** do you feel now?

Aya: I **was / were** very sick yesterday. I still feel sick today.

Supervisor: You can **bring / brings** your laptop home. You can work when you're feeling better.

Aya: Thank you. I'll have the report tomorrow.

2. The supervisor made a good decision.   True   False

C Aya talks to a co-worker. Complete the conversation.
Cross out the incorrect information. Then circle *True* or *False*.

1. Aya: What's wrong, Sam? You don't look well.

Co-worker: My head **hurt / hurts** this morning.

Aya: Are you better now?

Co-worker: I took some medicine for the headache, but now I **feel / feels** very sleepy.

Aya: You **should / shouldn't** tell the supervisor. You should probably **go / goes** home.

Co-worker: I guess you're right. I'm not **doing / do** very good work right now.

2. Aya's co-worker isn't making a good decision.   True   False

D JOB INFORMATION. Aya is an office assistant. She makes phone calls and answers emails. She also plans meetings and helps organize projects. Choose the correct answers.

1. Aya needs to speak to people every day.   True   False

2. Aya needs to have computer skills.   True   False

Unit 12: Help Wanted

Lesson 1: Vocabulary

A Look at the pictures. Complete the sentences. Use words from the box.

~~answers the phone~~	helps customers	takes care of grounds
drives a truck	uses a cash register	makes food

1. An office assistant ___*answers the phone*___.

2. A truck driver _____.

3. A landscaper _____.

4. A sales assistant _____.

5. A cook _____.

6. A cashier _____.

B Look at the pictures. What are the people doing now? Use words in the box.

making copies	~~taking care of children~~	using a computer
supervising workers	fixing things	working on a building

1. _She's taking care of children_ .

2. _____ .

3. _____ .

4. _____ .

5. _____ .

6. _____ .

C Which word doesn't belong? Cross it out.

1. drive	a truck	a car	a bus	~~a computer~~
2. use	a computer	a copy machine	a calculator	a message
3. take care of	grounds	children	people	boxes
4. fix	a computer	furniture	children	a refrigerator
5. make	food	cabinets	homework	copies

Lessons 2 & 3: Listening and Grammar

A Complete the sentences. Use words from the box.

write	make	speak	take	use	work	~~organize~~	help

1. Mandy ___can organize___ things.

2. She _____ a cash register.

3. He _____ returns.

4. Sol _____ reports.

5. Alf _____ with numbers.

6. Rob _____ cabinets.

7. Karl _____ customers.

8. Suni _____ English.

B ▶ Listen. Write *can* or *can't*.

1. Marcy has class tomorrow. She ___can't___ work.

2. Joe is a good cook. He _____ make great pizza.

3. Gwen is sick. She _____ go to class tonight.

4. I'm going to work now. I _____ drive you to school.

5. I'm good at my job. I _____ work with numbers and write reports.

6. Will is leaving the office now. He _____ pick up the package for you.

7. They're accountants. They _____ help you with your report.

8. He's a good employee, but he _____ write reports well.

C Look at the pictures. Write sentences.

1. <u>He can drive a truck</u>.

2. _____.

3. _____.

4. _____.

5. _____.

6. _____.

D What about you? What can you do? What can't you do?

I can _____.

I can't _____.

Lesson 4: Workplace, Life, and Community Skills

A ▶ Listen. Which job is the man calling about? Circle the letter.

A.	**B.**	**C.**
Office assistant	**Office assistant**	**Office assistant**
PT	PT	FT
10 hrs. wk.	M-TH 9 – 12pm	Wed – Sun 12 – 8pm
$12 hr	$12 hr	$12 hr
Exp. Nec.	Call Mr. Rogers	Call Devon
Call 413 555-7676	413 555-3200	413 555-2598

B Look at the jobs in Exercise A. Cross out the incorrect words.

1. Job A is a **part-time / ~~full-time~~** job.

2. Job B pays **$9 / $12** an hour.

3. Job C is a **part-time / full-time** job.

4. **Job A / Job B** is 12 hours a week.

5. You need experience for **Job A / Job C**.

6. You can call Devon about **Job B / Job C**.

C Read the descriptions about the people. Which job in Exercise A is good for them?

Job

1. Marie can't work on weekends. Her daughter finishes school at 12:30.   _____

2. Bob takes classes on Mondays and Tuesdays. He needs money for school.
He wants to work full-time.   _____

3. Laura has a part-time job on Mondays and Thursdays. She needs another
part-time job. She has experience in an office.   _____

D Answer the questions about the ads.

A.

SALES ASSISTANT

Office Barn is looking for full-time sales assistant.

First and second shifts. $10.50/hour.

40 hours/week.

You don't need experience.

APPLY NOW

B.

STOCK CLERKS

Better-for-You Foods is looking for part-time stock clerks.

Second and third shifts available.

You don't need experience.

$12.00/hour.

APPLY NOW

C.

ASSISTANT CHILD-CARE WORKER

Rainbow Daycare is looking for a part-time child-care worker for the first shift. The hours are Monday – Friday from 7 to 11 a.m. $9.00/hour. You need one year experience.

Email résumé to Mary@Rainbowdaycare.com

1. Shari wants to work at night. Which job is good for her? _____Job B_____

2. How much does the sales assistant make in one week? _____$420_____

3. Marco needs a part-time job after school. He can work in the afternoon.

   Which job is good for him? _____

4. Janeen loves children. She babysits often. Which job is good for her? _____

5. Carlo needs a full-time job. Which job is good for him? _____

6. Frank can work in the morning. He doesn't have work experience.

   Which job is good for him? _____

7. How much money does the child-care worker make in one week? _____

E What about you? If you don't work, answer the questions about school.

Do you work? _____

Do you work full-time or part-time? _____

How many hours do you work? _____

What days do you work? _____

Do you work nights? _____

Lessons 5 & 6: Listening and Grammar

A Look at the pictures. Complete the conversations

1. **A:** ___Can he___ fix computers?

   B: ___No, he can't___.

2. **A:** _____ drive a truck?

   B: _____.

3. **A:** _____ cook?

   B: _____.

4. **A:** _____ make furniture?

   B: _____.

5. **A:** _____ use a cash register?

   B: _____.

6. **A:** _____ lift the stove?

   B: _____.

B Look at Ester's schedule. Ask questions about when she can work

Mon.	Tues.	Wed.	Thurs.	Fri.	Sat.	Sun.
10 – 2	3 – 8	10 – 2	3 – 8	7 – 10	9 - 11	
Class	Babysit Justin	Class	Babysit	Dance	Soccer	

1. (Saturdays)

   A: _Can you work on Saturdays?_   **B:** _No, I can't._

2. (Sundays)

   A: _____   **B:** _____

3. (Monday nights)

   A: _____   **B:** _____

4. (Tuesday nights)

   A: _____   **B:** _____

5. (Friday nights)

   A: _____   **B:** _____

6. (Wednesday mornings)

   A: _____   **B:** _____

C Complete the conversation. Choose the correct questions from the box.

Can you use a computer?	~~OK. Which job?~~
Can you answer the phone?	Can you start now?

A: I'm here about a job. I noticed the Help Wanted sign.

B: _OK. Which job?_

A: The cashier's job. I can use a cash register.

B: _____

A: No, I can't, but I can learn.

B: _____

A: Sure. I can answer the phone.

B: _____

A: Yes, I can!

D ▶ Listen. Check your answers to Exercise C.

Lesson 7: Reading

A ▶ Listen and read.

ONLINE JOB SEARCH

Today, online job search sites can help you find a job. They list many jobs from companies, newspapers, and other sources.

How do you find a job online? First, think about
5 what kind of job you want. Maybe you already have experience for a particular job.

Next, you should write a résumé. A résumé describes you. It includes your education and your job experience. You can upload your résumé
10 to the job site. Employers can find you on the site.

You can also search for jobs near your home. Type in your zip code and then search. When you find a job that is interesting to you, you can apply online. Just click the button!

Your Job Finder

LOOKING FOR A JOB?

WHERE?   **WHAT?**

POST YOUR RESUME.

B DEVELOP YOUR ACADEMIC SKILLS. Read the Academic Skill. Look at the text. Find the circled words and the underlined words.

> **Academic Skill: Mark up a text**
> When you read an article the second time, mark it up for the important words or information. Circle important words and underline sentences. Try using different colors.

1. The underlined words are _____ of the circled words.

   a. a definition   **b.** examples

C CITE EVIDENCE. Complete the sentences. Where is the information? Write the line number.

Lines

1. An online job search site gets job listings from _____.
   a. the internet   **b.** companies   **c.** employees   _____

2. The first step to find a job is to find a job _____.
   a. that interests you   **b.** that pays well   **c.** that has good benefits   _____

3. The next step in the job search process is to write _____.
   a. a cover letter   **b.** a résumé   **c.** notes about your experience   _____

4. After you finish your résumé, you should _____.
   a. upload it   **b.** email it   **c.** make a copy of it   _____

5. If you want to find a job near your home on the job site, you can type

   your _____, and then click Search.
   a. phone number   **b.** zip code   **c.** area code   _____

Lessons 8 & 9: Listening and Grammar

A Complete the conversations. Use *was, wasn't, were,* or *weren't.*

1. **A:** ___Were___ you a student last year?   **B:** Yes, I ___was___.
2. **A:** _____ she a cook?   **B:** No, she _____.
3. **A:** _____ they in the U.S. last year?   **B:** No, they _____.
4. **A:** _____ your brothers carpenters?   **B:** No, they _____.
5. **A:** _____ it busy there?   **B:** Yes, it _____.
6. **A:** How long _____ you there?   **B:** Five years.
7. **A:** How long _____ Robert there?   **B:** Two years.
8. **A:** How long _____ they servers?   **B:** Three years.
9. **A:** What _____ your job?   **B:** I _____ a cashier.
10. **A:** What _____ her job?   **B:** She _____ a server.

B Unscramble the words to make questions.

1. _Were your parents in Colombia last year?_
   (were / in / Colombia /your parents / year / last)

2. _____
   (long / was / she / caregiver / how / a)

3. _____
   (job / her / what / at / store / was)

4. _____
   (Ms. Roberts / sick / last / was / week)

5. _____
   (nurse / you / were / a / that / in / hospital)

6. _____
   (his / full-time / was / job)

Lesson 10: Writing

A Read the Writing Skill. Circle the subjects. Underline the verbs.

1. (Mr. King) can make furniture.

2. She can't write reports.

3. I can work with numbers.

4. My last job was at a restaurant.

5. His job interview was last Wednesday.

> **Writing Skill: Recognize and use subjects**
>
> In English, every sentence has a subject.
> For example,
> (She) can write reports.

B Read the paragraph. Add job skills.

| phones | copies | a computer |

I have a job interview tomorrow. I have a lot of experience. I work in an office now. I can use _____. I can make _____. I can also answer _____. I want to learn more about computers. I want to start my own online company selling photos.

C Read the text. Correct four errors with verbs.

I want a job in technology. I can computers. I can also cell phones. I have experience in technology. I was a repair person at an electronics store. I there for two years. Now I work in an office. I can't writing well in English, but I can learn.

Lesson 11: Soft Skills at Work

A RESPOND WELL TO FEEDBACK. Cross out the incorrect words.

If a person responds well to feedback, he or she

learns from / doesn't change after it.

Kai has a new job at a hospital. He is a custodian.

B Kai talks to his supervisor. Cross out the incorrect words.
Then circle *True* or *False*.

1. Kai: Good morning, Ms. Smith.

Supervisor: Good morning, Kai. Well done! You did **good / bad** work today. I know that you're new. Are you enjoying the job?

Kai: **Yes / No.** I love it!

Supervisor: I **can / can't** understand that you have a lot to learn.

Kai: I'm **trying / try** to do my best.

Supervisor: Well, keep doing well!

2. Kai responds well to feedback.   True   False

C Kai talks to his supervisor. Cross out the incorrect words.
Then circle *True* or *False*.

1. Supervisor: Excuse me, Kai. **Were / Where** you on a break?

Kai: Yes, I **was / were.**

Supervisor: Can you please tell me when you take a break? You should **tell / telling** someone.

Kai: Oh, I'm sorry Ms. Smith. Yes, I **can / can't** do that.

Supervisor: Thank you.

Kai: I will tell a **co-worker / my friend** next time.

2. Kai doesn't respond well to feedback.   True   False

D JOB INFORMATION. **Kai is a custodian. He makes sure things are clean. He uses tools and machines to help him do his job. Choose the correct answers.**

1. Kai has to think about safety.   True   False

2. Kai's job is making sure things look nice.   True   False

Audio Script

UNIT 1

Page 3, Exercise D

Marta: Hi, I'm Marta.
Celia: Hi, Marta. I'm Celia.
Marta: Nice to meet you, Celia.
Celia: Nice to meet you, too.
Marta: Where are you from?
Celia: I'm from Brazil. What about you?
Marta: I'm from Peru.

Page 4, Exercise A

1. A: What's your first name?
   B: It's Casandra.
   A: How do you spell that?
   B: C-A-S-A-N-D-R-A.
2. A: And what's your last name?
   B: It's Balaban.
   A: How do you spell that?
   B: B-A-L-A-B-A-N.
3. A: What's your first name?
   B: It's Michael.
   A: How do you spell that?
   B: M-I-C-H-A-E-L.
4. A: And what's your last name?
   B: It's Oelbaum.
   A: How do you spell that?
   B: O-E-L-B-A-U-M.
5. A: What's your first name?
   B: It's Polina.
   A: How do you spell that?
   B: P-O-L-I-N-A.
6. A: And what's your last name?
   B: It's Sidorov.
   A: How do you spell that?
   B: S-I-D-O-R-O-V.

Page 4, Exercise B

1. A: What's your first name?
   B: My first name is Allie.
   A: How do you spell that?
   B: A-L-L-I-E.
   A: And what's your last name?
   B: Sampson.
   A: S-A-M-S-O-N?
   B: No. S-A-M-P-S-O-N.
   A: Is that Ms. or Mrs.?
   B: Ms.
2. A: Your first name, please?
   B: My first name is Rodrigo.
   A: How do you spell that?
   B: R-O-D-R-I-G-O.
   A: And what's your last name?
   B: Ferreira.
   A: How do you spell that?

B: F-E-R-R-E-I-R-A.
   A: Thank you.
3. A: Can you tell me your first name, please?
   B: My first name is Svetlana.
   A: How do you spell that?
   B: S-V-E-T-L-A-N-A.
   A: And what's your last name?
   B: Jones.
   A: J-O-N-E-S?
   B: Yes.
   A: Is that Ms. or Mrs.?
   B: Mrs.

Page 10, Exercise E

Rob: Who's that?
Ana: That's the teacher.
Sue: That's not the teacher.
Ana: You're right. That's Mila.
Rob: Where's she from?
Ana: She's from Russia. She's in Level 1.
Rob: Who's that?
Ana: That's Juan.
Sue: That's not Juan.
Ana: You're right. That's Mr. Jones.
Rob: Where's he from?
Ana: He's from the United States. He's the teacher.
     He's great.

UNIT 2

Page 16, Exercise D

Mike: Sonia, this is Marie. Marie, this is Sonia.
Sonia: Hi, Marie. It's nice to meet you.
Marie: Nice to meet you, too, Sonia.
Sonia: So, Marie, what do you do?
Marie: I'm an office assistant. What about you?
Sonia: I'm an office assistant, too.
Marie: Oh, that's interesting.

Page 17, Exercise A

1. three	3. eight	5. zero	7. five	9. four
2. six	4. one	6. nine	8. seven	10. two

Page 17, Exercise C

1. (903) 555-3460	4. (302) 555-7981
2. (302) 555-6092	5. (302) 555-8132
3. (903) 555-8416	

Page 18, Exercise E

1. A: Directory Assistance.
   B: What's the number for The Blue Moon Restaurant?
   A: The number is (473) 555-3442.
   B: Thank you.
2. A: Directory Assistance.

B: What's the number for Kay's Clothes Store?
A: The number is (473) 555-8976.
B: Thank you.
3. A: Directory Assistance.
   B: What's the number for Mountainville Hospital?
   A: The number is (473) 555-7840.
   B: Thank you.
4. A: Directory Assistance.
   B: What's the number for The Peamont Child-Care Center?
   A: The number is (473) 555-4738.
   B: Thank you.
5. A: Directory Assistance.
   B: What's the number for Shelburn Office Supplies?
   A: The number is (473) 555-9267.
   B: Thank you.

Page 20, Exercise C

1. A: What does Calvin do?
   B: He's a cook.
2. A: What does Ms. Torres do?
   B: She's a child-care worker.
3. A: What does Hong-Yi do?
   B: He's an electrician.
4. A: What does Kristina do?
   B: She's an accountant.
5. A: What does Daniel do?
   B: He's an office assistant.
6. A: What does Elena do?
   B: She's an accountant.
7. A: What does Rodrigo do?
   B: He's an artist.
8. A: What does Kim do?
   B: She's a child-care worker.
9. A: What does Robert do?
   B: He's a cook.

Page 22, Exercise C

a. She works in a restaurant. She's a cook.
b. She works in a store. She's a stock clerk.
c. He works in a nursing home. He's a caregiver.
d. She works at a factory. She's an assembly-line worker.

UNIT 3

Page 33, Exercise C

1. A: What room is the cafeteria?
   B: It's Room 17.
2. A: What room is the computer lab?
   B: It's Room 23.
3. A: What room is the library?
   B: It's Room 28.
4. A: What room is the main office?
   B: It's Room 19.

Page 35, Exercise E

Bob: Excuse me. Can you help me?
Meg: Sure.
Bob: What room is the ESL office?
Meg: Sorry. I don't know. Ask him.
Bob: Uh . . . who's he?
Meg: That's Mr. Smith, the custodian.
Bob: Excuse me. Which way is the ESL office?
Mr. Smith: It's down the hall on the left, Room 24.
Bob: Thank you.
Mr. Smith: You're welcome.

UNIT 4

Page 41, Exercise F

Eva: That's a great photo. Who's that?
Tom: That's my sister, Fran.
Eva: She looks nice. Is that your mother?
Tom: Yes, it is.
Eva: Fran looks like her.
Tom: Yes. And this is my brother, Tim.
Eva: He looks like your mother, too.
Tom: I know. And I look like my father.

Page 44, Exercise F

Mary: Is your family here in this country?
Luz: Well, my brother and sister are here. My parents are in Mexico.
Mary: What's your brother like?
Luz: He's great.
Mary: Does he look like you?
Luz: Yes. He's tall and thin and has short hair.
Mary: What about your sister? Does she look like you?
Luz: No. She's average height and heavy. She has long hair.

Page 46, Exercise B

A: How old are your children?
B: I have two boys and a girl. My son, José, is 14. He's in the ninth grade.
A: OK. So he's in the ninth grade.
B: Yes. Then, Carmen is 11.
A: So, she's in the fifth grade?
B: No. She's in the sixth grade.
A: Sorry. The sixth grade. And your third child? How old is he?
B: Miguel is eight. He's in the third grade.

Page 47, Exercise E

Mark: Hi, Nina. Where are you?
Nina: I'm at my cousin's house. I'm babysitting for her kids.
Mark: Oh, that's nice. How old are they?
Nina: Well, her daughter is nine. She's in the fourth

grade. And her son is seven. He's in the second grade.

UNIT 5

Page 53, Exercise C

1. A: How much is the blouse?
   B: It's $24.95.
2. A: How much are the shoes?
   B: They're $37.50.
3. A: How much is the T-shirt?
   B: It's $14.99.
4. A: How much are the socks?
   B: They're $9.95.
5. A: How much is the wallet?
   B: It's $34.50.
6. A: How much are the pants?
   B: They're $49.99.

Page 56, Exercise D

Mother: Linda, look at the sale! Do you need clothes for school?
Linda: Yes, I do. I need T-shirts.
Mother: Well, they have T-shirts in green, yellow, and blue.
Linda: I like the blue T-shirts.
Mother: You need black pants. Do they have them?
Linda: Yes, they do. I like these black pants.
Mother: Do they have a small?
Linda: Yes, they do. Here they are.
Mother: And the jackets are great. You need a new jacket, too. Do you like this jacket?
Linda: No, I don't.
Mother: OK.

UNIT 6

Page 65, Exercise C

1. There's an old kitchen.
2. There's a sunny bedroom.
3. It's a cheap house.
4. There's a large bathroom.

Page 68, Exercise A

1. 365 Meadow Drive
2. 52 Park Boulevard
3. 45 Orange Avenue
4. 37 Sutton Street
5. 145 Drake Road

Page 69, Exercise E

1. A: Is there a one-bedroom apartment available?
   B: Yes, there is.
   A: How much is it?
   B: It's $1,200 a month.

A: Does it have a new kitchen?
B: No, it doesn't, but it has a large kitchen with a new stove.
A: Does it have parking?
B: Yes, it has parking.
A: What's the address?
B: It's 14 Bank Street, Apartment 3D.

2. A: Is there a two-bedroom apartment available?
   B: Yes, there is.
   A: How much is it?
   B: It's $1,300 a month.
   A: Does it have a large bathroom?
   B: Yes, it does. It has a large bathroom with a new shower.
   A: What's the address?
   B: It's 346 Clover Boulevard, Apartment 1C.
3. A: Is there a three-bedroom apartment for rent?
   B: Yes, there is. And the building is new.
   A: How much is it?
   B: It's $1,450 a month.
   A: Does it have a dining room?
   B: Yes, there's a large dining room.
   A: What's the address?
   B: 45 Orchard Avenue, Apartment 2B.
4. A: Is there a one-bedroom apartment for rent?
   B: Yes, there is.
   A: How much is it?
   B: It's $900 a month.
   A: Is there a dining room?
   B: No, but there's a large living room.
   A: Does it have laundry and parking?
   B: It doesn't have parking. But there's a laundry room in the building.
   A: What's the address?
   B: 3 Apple Drive, Apartment 2A.

Page 71, Exercise D

Go north on Powell Street. Continue on Powell Street for three blocks. Turn right at the 2nd light. Continue east on Starrett Street. Our store is on Starrett Street on the right. It's at 3228 Starrett Street.

UNIT 7

Page 78, Exercise A

A: Hi, Marie. Are you free for lunch any day this week?
B: Gee, I'm not sure. I have a very busy schedule this week.
A: Well, how about Tuesday?
B: Oh, no, sorry. You know, I work on Tuesdays and Thursdays from 10:00 to 2:00.
A: Oh, too bad. How about Wednesday?
B: Oh, no, sorry. On Wednesdays I have English class from 1:00 to 5:00. Oh, wait. Friday is good. I'm free on Friday!

Page 83, Exercise B

A: So, Ms. Jones, can you tell us what activities you do to relax?
B: Well, I exercise.
A: Really? How often do you exercise?
B: I go running three times a week.
A: Great!
B: And I take a long walk once a week.
A: Oh, that's good.
B: And I do puzzles.
A: How often do you do puzzles?
B: Every day. I love puzzles.
A: Great. What about music? How often do you listen to music?
B: Oh, never. I never listen to music.

UNIT 8

Page 91, Exercise B

A: Can I help you?
B: Yes, I'd like to order a green salad.
A: OK.
B: I'd like a hamburger, too.
A: OK. A green salad and a hamburger. Anything else?
B: Yes, please. An order of fries.
A: Large or small?
B: Large, please.
A: Anything to drink?
B: Yes, a large soda.
A: OK. And what would you like, sir?
C: I'd like a bowl of soup.
A: A bowl of soup. OK. Anything else?
C: A chicken sandwich and a baked potato, please.
A: A chicken sandwich and a baked potato. OK. Would you like anything to drink?
C: A large iced tea, please.
A: OK. Anything else?
C: Oh, yes. Apple pie.
A: Apple pie. OK.

Page 93, Exercise C

Welcome shoppers. Today at Foodmart we have specials in every department. This week only we have green beans on sale for just $1.19 a pound. That's right—just $1.19 a pound.
We also have potatoes on sale for just 79¢ a pound. In our fish and seafood department we have fresh fish for just $3.99 a pound. And in our meat department we have chicken on sale for just $3.59 a pound. And go to our bakery to find bread on sale for $2.99. Thanks for shopping at Foodmart this week.

Page 95, Exercise C

A: Let's have grilled chicken and rice.
B: And I can make a large green salad.
A: Yes, and for drinks, we can serve water, juice, and soda.
B: That sounds good. What else do we need?
A: A dessert? Can you make apple pie?
B: Sure. I'll make two apple pies.

UNIT 9

Page 104, Exercise D

Ann: Are you watching the news?
Tim: No, I'm not. I'm reading a magazine.
Ann: Well, turn on the TV. A big storm is coming.
Tim: Really?
Ann: Yes. In fact, I'm coming home early. I'm at the grocery store now.
Tim: Oh, good. Are you getting water?
Ann: Yes. I'm getting water, food, and a lot of batteries.
Tim: Great. Get matches, too.
Ann: OK. Do we need anything else?
Tim: Yes. We need good weather!

Page 107, Exercise C

1. In San Francisco it's cool and very foggy today.
2. In Seattle it's rainy and pretty cool—only 58°.
3. It's a beautiful day in New York. It's sunny and pretty warm for March—72°.
4. It's another hot and humid day in Houston. It's really humid and the temperature is already 86°.
5. Denver has perfect weather for making snowmen. It's not snowing, but it's very cold—18°.

UNIT 10

Page 115, Exercise B

Meg: How do you get to the high school?
Rob: Take the Number 12 train.
Meg: OK. Where do you get the train?
Rob: Around the corner on Colombo Road.
Meg: Great. Where do you buy a ticket?
Rob: In the station.
Meg: Thanks. One more question. How much does the train cost?
Rob: $2.50.

Page 115, Exercise D

Mark: Which bus goes to the high school?
Lisa: The Number 27 bus goes to the high school.
Mark: OK. What time does the bus leave the station?
Lisa: At 7:15.
Mark: How much does the bus cost?
Lisa: $3.50.
Mark: Thanks. One more question. Where do you get off?
Lisa: Dupont Square.

Page 119, Exercise D

There are plenty of fun things happening in our area this weekend. There's a new movie opening at the Howlie Theater. *Sands of Time* has shows on Friday and Saturday night at 7:30, 9:50, and 11:15. If it's sports you're after, the Vikings are playing soccer at the high school on Sunday afternoon. The game starts at 3 P.M. If you like rock music, the Heavenly Six are playing in town on Saturday night. The concert begins at 8 P.M.

UNIT 11

Page 126, Exercise A

Cathy: Good morning. Dr. Russo's office. This is Cathy.
Lucy: Hi, Cathy. This is Lucy Peterson. I'd like to make an appointment with Dr. Russo.
Cathy: Sure. What day?
Lucy: Does he have anything on Wednesday?
Cathy: Hmm. No, I'm sorry. How about Thursday morning?
Lucy: OK. Thursday morning is good. What time?
Cathy: How's 10:30?
Lucy: That's fine.
Cathy: OK. That's Thursday, May 14th, at 10:30. See you then.

Page 128, Exercise A

1. I was sick yesterday. I wasn't at work.
2. Carlos wasn't at home last night. He was at his cousin's house.
3. Mari wasn't absent last night. She was in class.
4. We were sick last week. We weren't in school.
5. They weren't in class yesterday. They were sick.

Page 130, Exercise A

1. A: I have a bad headache.
   B: You should drink water.
2. A: He has the flu.
   B: He shouldn't go to school today.
3. A: We have colds.
   B: You should drink a lot of juice.
4. A: Ms. Moyer has a backache.
   B: She shouldn't go running.
5. A: She has a bad cough.
   B: She should drink tea and honey.
6. A: Mr. Moore has a fever.
   B: He shouldn't go to work.

Page 130, Exercise C

Sara: Hi, Joe. This is Sara.
Joe: Hi, Sara. How are you? Is something wrong?
Sara: Well, I'm sick. I'm not coming to work today.
Joe: Oh, I'm sorry to hear that. What do you have?

Sara: I'm not sure. I have a headache, and my stomach doesn't feel good.
Joe: Do you have a fever?
Sara: Yes, I do. I just feel terrible.
Joe: Well, take it easy, Sara. You should rest and drink a lot.
Sara: That's a good idea.
Joe: But call the doctor if you don't feel better soon. You really shouldn't wait too long.
Sara: OK. Thanks Joe.

UNIT 12

Page 136, Exercise B

1. Marcy has class tomorrow. She can't work.
2. Joe is a good cook. He can make great pizza.
3. Gwen is sick. She can't go to class tonight.
4. I'm going to work now. I can't drive you to school.
5. I'm good at my job. I can work with numbers and write reports.
6. Will is leaving the office now. He can pick up the package for you.
7. They're accountants. They can help you with your report.
8. He's a good employee, but he can't write reports well.

Page 138, Exercise A

A: Colony Real Estate. How can I help you?
B: I'm calling about the ad in the paper today.
A: Which ad?
B: The ad for an office assistant.
A: Oh, yes. Do you have office experience?
B: Yes, I do. And the hours are on Fridays and Saturdays?
A: Yes. Fridays and Saturdays from 10 to 3.
B: And it pays $12 an hour?
A: Yes, that's right. Can you use a computer?
B: Yes, I can use a computer.
A: Great! Why don't you come in this afternoon at 3:00?
B: OK. Thanks.

Page 141, Exercise D

A: I'm here about a job. I noticed the Help Wanted sign.
B: OK. Which job?
A: The cashier's job. I can use a cash register.
B: Can you use a computer?
A: No, I can't. But I can learn.
B: Can you answer the phone?
A: Sure. I can answer the phone.
B: Can you start now?
A: Yes, I can.
B: Great! You can have the job! Welcome to Yao's Chinese Restaurant

Answer Key

UNIT 1

Page 2, Exercise A

1. The United States
2. Mexico
3. Canada
4. Peru
5. Cuba
6. Brazil
7. El Salvador
8. Iraq
9. Poland
10. Somalia
11. China
12. South Korea
13. Russia
14. Ethiopia
15. Vietnam

Page 2, Exercise B

Answers may vary. Possible answers include:

1. Canada
2. South Korea
3. Poland
4. Iraq
5. Peru
6. El Salvador
7. Somalia

Page 3, Exercise A

1. I'm from Poland.
2. I'm from El Salvador.
3. I'm from Vietnam.
4. I'm from South Korea.

Page 3, Exercise B

1. Sofi Kolski is from Poland.
2. Debra Leon is from El Salvador.
3. Min Dong is from Vietnam.
4. Sun Kim is from South Korea.

Page 3, Exercise C

4	Nice to meet you, too.
2	Hi, Marta. I'm Celia.
3	Nice to meet you, Celia.
5	Where are you from?
6	I'm from Brazil. What about you?
1	Hi, I'm Marta.
7	I'm from Peru.

Page 4, Exercise A

1. Casandra
2. Balaban
3. Michael
4. Oelbaum
5. Polina
6. Sidorov

Page 4, Exercise B

1. Ms. Allie Sampson
2. Mr. Rodrigo Ferreira
3. Mrs. Svetlana Jones

Page 5, Exercise C

1. Amelia
2. Ava
3. Charlotte
4. Emma
5. Isabella
6. Mia
7. Olivia
8. Sophia

Page 5, Exercise D

1. Miss Jones
2. Mr. Kaz
3. Miss. Cabo
4. Mrs. Lin

Page 6, Exercise A

1. am / am
2. is / is
3. is / is

Page 6, Exercise B

1. She is from Peru.
2. He is from Iraq.
3. He is from the United States.
4. She is from South Korea.

Page 6, Exercise C

1. She's   3. He's
2. She's   4. He's

Page 7, Exercise D

1. Katya is not in Level 2. She's in Level 1.
2. Mani is not from El Salvador. He's from Mexico.

3. Mr. Fani is not the teacher. He's a student.
4. I am not in Level 3. I'm in Level 1.

Page 7, Exercise E

1. Ms. Cabral is not from China. She's from Brazil.
2. Mr. Duval is not in Level 2. He's in Level 1.
3. Mrs. Gao is not from Vietnam. She's from China.
4. Mr. Medina is not from Brazil. He's from Mexico.
5. Mr. Molev is not in Level 2. He's in Level 3.
6. Ms. Park is not in Level 3. She's in Level 2.

Page 8, Exercise A

1. "Where Immigrants Live in the U.S."
2. c.

Page 8, Exercise C

1. c. Lines 10-12
2. b. Lines 13-14

Page 8, Exercise D

1. c   2. b

Page 9, Exercise A

1. are / They're in Level 2.
2. are / We're students.
3. are / You're a student.
4. are / We're from Russia.
5. are / They're in Level 3.
6. is / It's interesting.

Page 9, Exercise B

1. We are from El Salvador.
2. We are in Level 2.
3. Tomas and Celia are from Brazil.
4. You are a student.
5. Tania and I are absent today.

Page 9, Exercise C

1. d   2. c   3. b   4. a

Page 10, Exercise D

1. They're not in Level 4.
2. We're not from Somalia.
3. My English class isn't hard.
4. Mr. and Mrs. Kim aren't from China.
5. Celia and I aren't students.
6. Calvin and Ricardo aren't from El Salvador.
7. Diego and Armando aren't students.
8. This book isn't interesting.

Page 10, Exercise E

Rob: Who's that?
Ana: That's _the teacher_.
Sue: That's _not_ the teacher.
Ana: You're right. That's Mila.
Rob: Where's _she_ from?
Ana: _She's_ from Russia. _She's_ in Level 1.
Rob: Who's that?
Ana: That's Juan.
Sue: That's _not_ Juan.
Ana: You're right. That's Mr. Jones.
Rob: Where's _he_ from?
Ana: _He's_ from the United States. _He's_ the teacher. _He's_ great.

Page 11, Exercise A

1. She isn't in my class.
2. Bob and Al aren't absent.
3. The teacher isn't interesting.
4. The students aren't friendly.
5. Level 2 isn't hard.

Page 11, Exercise B

1. It isn't easy. It's hard.
2. She isn't from India. She's from Somalia.
3. He isn't in Level 2. He's in Level 3.
4. They aren't from Vietnam. They're from China.
5. They aren't from China. They're from South Korea.
6. David isn't in school. He's absent.

Page 12, Exercise A

1. My friend Suni is from (I)ndia.
2. (I)ndia is a country in (A)sia.
3. She's in (H)ouston, (T)exas now.
4. (S)uni is in the (G)reenville (A)dult (S)chool.
5. (M)s. (B)rown is the teacher.

Page 12, Exercise B

You use capital letters for the first word in a sentence.

Page 12, Exercise C

My name _is_ Min. I'_m_ from Hanoi, Vietnam. Vietnam _is_ in Asia. It _isn't_ a big country. It's small. Now I'm in San Francisco, California. I'_m_ in school now. My teacher _is_ Mr. Cooper. He'_s_ friendly. The students _are_ also friendly. I'_m_ happy here.

Page 12, Exercise D

Ms. Hale is my teacher. She's very interesting and friendly. She's from the United States. The students in my class are from India, China, and Mexico.

Page 13, Exercise A

a, b, d

Page 13, Exercise B

1. Aki: Hi, you're new, right?
   Sam: Hi. Yes, I ~~is~~ / am. I'm sorry. What's ~~you~~ / your name?
   Aki: I'm Aki. And what's / ~~how's~~ your name?
   Sam: I'm Sam. Nice to meet / ~~see~~ you, Aki.
   Aki: Nice to meet you ~~again~~ / too, Sam.
2. True

Page 13, Exercise C

1. Aki: Hi, I'm Aki.
   Ana: Hi.
   Aki: Nice / ~~new~~ to meet you.

Ana: Yes.
Aki: What's / ~~Is~~ your name?
Ana: Ana.
2. False

Page 13, Exercise D

1. True   2. True

UNIT 2
Page 14, Exercise A

1. sales assistant
2. landscaper
3. homemaker
4. electrician
5. driver
6. nurse
7. child-care worker
8. doctor
9. manager

Page 14, Exercise B

1. sales assistant
2. driver
3. doctor
4. manager
5. homemaker
6. child-care worker
7. landscaper
8. nurse
9. electrician

Page 15, Exercise C

1. doctor
2. cashier
3. server
4. cook

Page 15, Exercise D

1. accountant
2. painter
3. office assistant
4. electrician

Page 16, Exercise A

1. a   3. a   5. a
2. a   4. a   6. an

Page 16, Exercise B

1. Paul and Rafael are doctors.
2. Carla and Luke are servers.
3. Marco and Tania are nurses.
4. Liam and Sal are landscapers.
5. Mia and Luz are accountants.
6. Kim and Mike are cashiers.

Page 16, Exercise C

Mike: Sonia, this is Marie. Marie, this is Sonia.

Sonia: Hi, Marie. It's nice to meet you.

Marie: *Nice to meet you, too, Sonia.*

Sonia: So, Marie, what do you do?

Marie: *I'm an office assistant. What about you?*

Sonia: I'm an office assistant, too.

Marie: *Oh, that's interesting.*

Page 17, Exercise A

1. 3	6. 9
2. 6	7. 5
3. 8	8. 7
4. 1	9. 4
5. 0	10. 2

Page 17, Exercise B

1. three	6. nine
2. six	7. five
3. eight	8. seven
4. one	9. four
5. zero	10. two

Page 17, Exercise C

1. d   2. c   3. b   4. a   5. e

Page 18, Exercise D

1. (212) 555-3480
2. (718) 555-9322
3. smith555@hmail.com
4. (914) 555-4438
5. mike368@hmail.com

Page 18, Exercise E

The Blue Moon
  Restaurant: (473) 555-3442

Kay's Clothes
  Store: (473) 555-8976
Mountainville
  Hospital: (473) 555-7840
The Peamont Child-Care
  Center: (473) 555-4738
Shelburn Office
  Supplies: (473) 555-9267

Page 18, Exercise F

Answers will vary.

Page 19, Exercise A

1. Are / am
2. Is / isn't **OR** 's not
3. Is / isn't **OR** 's not
4. Are / aren't **OR** 're not
5. Are / 'm not

Page 19, Exercise B

1. A: Is Rob an electrician?
   B: Yes, he is.
2. A: Are Sarah and Ann cashiers?
   B: No, they aren't. **OR** No, they're not.
3. A: Is Mr. Ruiz a landscaper?
   B: Yes, he is.
4. A: Are Carl and Miguel cooks?
   B: Yes, they are.
5. A: Is Jason an accountant?
   B: No, he isn't. **OR** No, he's not.
6. A: Is Bianca a doctor?
   B: Yes, she is.

Page 20, Exercise C

1. cook
2. child-care worker
3. electrician
4. accountant
5. office assistant
6. accountant
7. artist
8. child-care worker
9. cook

Page 20, Exercise D

1. A: That's Calvin. He's a cook.
   B: *Is Kristina* a cook, too?
   A: *No, she isn't. She's an accountant.*

2. A: That's Daniel. He's an office assistant.
   B: *Is Ms. Torres an office assistant,* too?
   A: *No, she isn't. She's a child-care worker.*
3. A: That's Hong-Yi. He's an electrician.
   B: *Is Calvin an electrician,* too?
   A: *No, he isn't. He's a cook.*
4. A: That's Daniel. He's an office assistant.
   B: *Are Elena and Kristina office assistants,* too?
   A: *No, they're accountants.*

Page 21, Exercise B

1. b   2. a

Page 21, Exercise C

1. c. Line 1
2. a. Lines 3-4
3. b. Line 8

Page 21, Exercise D

1. a   2. b

Page 22, Exercise A

1. work / c
2. work / e
3. works / b
4. work / a
5. works / d

Page 22, Exercise B

1. work	4. works
2. work	5. work
3. works	6. works

Page 22, Exercise C

1. d   2. c   3. a   4. b

Page 23, Exercise D

1. are / live / works / work
2. is / works / lives
3. live / are / work

Page 23, Exercise E

Edna: _Hi, I'm Edna._
Sam: Hi, Edna. I'm Sam.
Edna: _It's nice to meet you._
Sam: It's nice to meet you, too.
Edna: _Are you a student here?_
Sam: No, I'm not. I'm a teacher.
Edna: _Really? That's interesting._
Sam: What do you do, Edna?
Edna: _I'm a nurse._
Sam: Really? Where do you work?
Edna: _I work in a nursing home._
Sam: That's great!

Page 24, Exercise A

1. Ms. Lin is a nurse at a nursing home.
2. Linda and Max work at a factory.
3. Fara is a caregiver at a hospital.
4. We are servers. We work at a restaurant on Main Street.
5. Matt is a carpenter. He works at the construction site.

Page 24, Exercise B

Nan Smith is my friend. She's a child-care worker. She works at Sunshine Day Care Center. She likes her job.

Page 24, Exercise C

Jack is my co-worker. We are stock clerks at Good Food Supermarket. It's a hard job. Jack lives in New York. I live in New York, too.

Page 25, Exercise A

a, b, d

Page 25, Exercise B

1. Supervisor: So, put these boxes away first. Then get the new boxes off the truck.
   Fredy: I'm ~~understand~~ / sorry. Could you please repeat / ~~too~~ that?

   Supervisor: Sure. First these boxes, and then the ones on the truck.
   Fredy: OK, I ~~do~~ / understand. Thank you.

2. a

Page 25, Exercise C

1. Co-worker: Who's that / ~~those?~~ Is that the landscaper?
   Fredy: No, she ~~is~~ / isn't. She's the electrician.
   Co-worker: Sorry. She is the electrician, right?
   Fredy: Yes, that's right / ~~nice.~~ She ~~work~~ / works at Main Electric.

2. b

Page 25, Exercise D

1. True   2. True

UNIT 3

Page 26, Exercise A

1. a notebook
2. a dictionary
3. a folder
4. an eraser
5. a piece of paper
6. a book
7. a sticky note
8. a phone

Page 27, Exercise B

1. a desk
2. a laptop
3. a three-ring binder
4. a backpack
5. a board
6. a projector

Page 27, Exercise C

1. a notebook / a pencil
2. a laptop / a book

3. a dictionary / a piece of paper
4. an eraser / a folder

Page 28, Exercise A

1. _Write_ in your notebooks.
2. _Take out_ a piece of paper.
3. _Turn off_ your cell phone.
4. _Put away_ your books.
5. Can I _borrow_ a pen?

Page 28, Exercise B

1. Don't look at the book
2. Don't write your name.
3. Don't open your dictionary.
4. Don't take out your notebook.
5. Don't use a pencil.
6. Don't put away your book.

Page 29, Exercise C

1. Don't use a pen.
2. Don't turn off your computer.
3. Don't take out your notebook.
4. Take out your book.
5. Don't look at your classmate's test.
6. Use a pencil.
7. Fill in the circles.
8. Use a dictionary.

Page 30, Exercise A

1. a   2. b

Page 30, Exercise C

1. c. Line 1-2
2. c. Line 7
3. b. Lines 16-17

Page 31, Exercise A

1. This   3. Those
2. These   4. That

Page 31, Exercise B

1. Those are great backpacks.
2. These are good markers.
3. Those are my books.
4. These are great keyboards.
5. These are my binders.
6. Those are good printers.

Page 31, Exercise C

1. That is your computer.
2. Those are great chairs.
3. This is my computer **OR** screen.
4. These are great books.

Page 32, Exercise D

1. A: *Is this* a screen?
   B: *Yes, it is.*
2. A: *Is that* a tablet?
   B: *No, it isn't / it's not. It's a mouse.*
3. A: *Is that* a laptop?
   B: *No, it isn't / it's not. It's a notebook.*
4. A: *Are those* markers?
   B: *Yes, they are.*
5. A: *Are those* erasers?
   B: *No, they're not / they aren't. They're notebooks.*
6. A: *Is that* a phone?
   B: *No, it isn't / it's not. It's a folder.*

Page 32, Exercise E

1. c   3. c   5. c   7. b
2. a   4. b   6. a

Page 33, Exercise A

1. Where is *the restroom*?
2. Where is *the cafeteria*
3. Where is *Room 114*?
4. Which way is *the Computer Lab*?
5. Which way is *Room 216*?

Page 33, Exercise B

1. It's across from the office.
2. It's next to Room 116.
3. It's across from the cafeteria **OR** It's across from Room 218.

Page 33, Exercise C

1. 17   2. 23   3. 28   4. 19

Page 34, Exercise A

1. her   4. him
2. him   5. her
3. her

Page 34, Exercise B

1. Please call her.
2. Don't open it.
3. Please help them.
4. How do you spell it?
5. Call her about the job.
6. Ask him for help.

Page 35, Exercise C

1. me   6. them
2. him   7. it
3. them   8. them
4. her   9. you
5. us   10. us

Page 35, Exercise D

Bob: Excuse me. *Can you help me?*
Meg: Sure.
Bob: *What room is the ESL office?*
Meg: Sorry. I don't know. Ask him.
Bob: Uh . . . Who's he?
Meg: *That's Mr. Smith, the custodian.*
Bob: Excuse me. Where is the ESL office?
Mr. Smith: *It's down the hall on the left, Room 24.*
Bob: Thank you.
Mr. Smith: You're welcome.

Page 36, Exercise A

1. Those (are) new laptops.
2. We (have) 18 desks in our classroom.
3. He (works) as a nurse at a hospital.
4. The computer lab (is) across from the office.
5. Please (put away) your phones.
6. These computers (are) old.
7. The office (is) open at 9.
8. They (have) new laptops in their office.

Page 36, Exercise B

I <u>practice</u> English at work. I <u>work</u> at a computer store three days a week. I <u>listen</u> to the manager. I <u>speak</u> with my co-workers. This <u>gives</u> me practice speaking English. I also <u>study</u>. After work I <u>have</u> English class. I <u>do</u> my homework during my break. Sometimes my co-workers <u>help</u> me.

Page 36, Exercise C

I study English at school three mornings a week. First, we read our books. We <u>answer</u> the questions in the book. I write the new words. We talk about the reading. Then we listen to the teacher and he <u>answers</u> our questions. We <u>listen</u> to a podcast. I get a lot of practice with English in my class.

Page 37, Exercise A

A person who is flexible likes / ~~doesn't like~~ to change.

Page 37, Exercise B

1. Ying: Do you work / ~~works~~ next Saturday?
   Co-worker: No, I ~~do~~ / don't.
   Ying: OK. ~~Can't~~ / Can you work that Saturday? I can't work.
   Co-worker: Yes, I can / ~~work~~. No problem.
   Ying: Thank you!
2. True

Page 37, Exercise C

1. Co-worker: Hi Ying. Is ~~these~~ / this your pen?
   Ying: Yes, it is / ~~are~~.
   Co-worker: Can I borrow / ~~put away~~ it?
   Ying: Sure, here you go. I can use a different one.
2. True

Page 37, Exercise D

1. False   2. True

UNIT 4

Page 38, Exercise A

1. parents
2. husband
3. daughter
4. sister
5. children
6. mother
7. wife
8. brother
9. son
10. grandfather
11. grandmother
12. father

Page 38, Exercise B

Male: father, son, grandfather, brother, husband
Female: daughter, grandmother, sister, wife
Male and Female: parents, children

Page 39, Exercise C

1. They're Dan's parents.
2. He's Dan's father.
3. She's Dan's mother.
4. She's Dan's wife.
5. They're Dan's children.
6. He's Dan's son.
7. She's Dan's daughter.

Page 39, Exercise D

1. He's my brother.
2. He's my grandfather.
3. She's my grandmother.
4. She's my sister.

Page 40, Exercise A

1. My   4. Her
2. Your   5. Their
3. His   6. our

Page 40, Exercise B

1. Edna is from Haiti. She looks like her / ~~their~~ sister.

2. Ivan and Oleg are brothers. Their / ~~His~~ parents are in Russia.
3. Marisa and ~~his~~ / her husband live in Brazil, but ~~his~~ / their children live in Los Angeles.
4. We're servers. The restaurant is across from ~~his~~ / our house.
5. Felix looks like ~~their~~ / his sister. They live with ~~our~~ / their parents.
6. Carlos and I are accountants. ~~Their~~ / Our office is across the street.

Page 40, Exercise C

1. my   4. his
2. their   5. his
3. her   6. his

Page 41, Exercise D

1. Jack's
2. Stanley's
3. Monica's
4. Molly's
5. Monica's

Page 41, Exercise E

Eva: That's a great photo. Who's that?
Tom: _That's my sister, Fran._
Eva: _She looks nice. Is that your mother?_
Tom: Yes, it is.
Eva: _Fran looks like her._
Tom: Yes. And this is my brother, Tim.
Eva: _He looks like your mother, too._
Tom: I know. And I look like my father.

Page 42, Exercise A

1. a   2. a

Page 42, Exercise C

1. a. Lines 3-4
2. a. Lines 7-8
3. b. Lines 10-12

Page 42, Exercise D

1. b   2. b

Page 43, Exercise A

1. has
2. is
3. are
4. am / have
5. is / has
6. is / has
7. are / have

Page 43, Exercise B

1. 's / has
2. has / 's
3. 's / has
4. 's / has
5. 's / has

Page 43, Exercise C

4, 5, 2, 1, 3

Page 44, Exercise D

Answers will vary. Possible answers include:
1. Pat is short and average weight. He has short hair.
2. Sam is tall and thin. He has a mustache and a beard. He has short hair.
3. Al is average height and heavy. He has long hair.

Page 44, Exercise E

Mary: _Is your family here in this country?_
Luz: Well, my brother and sister are here. My parents are in Mexico.
Mary: _What's your brother like?_
Luz: He's great.
Mary: _Does he look like you?_
Luz: Yes. He's tall and thin and has short hair.
Mary: What about your sister? _Does she look like you?_
Luz: No. She's average height and heavy. She has long hair.

Page 45, Exercise A

1. Jay's birthday is March 5.
2. Sue's birthday is March 8.
3. Linda's birthday is March 12.
4. Dave's birthday is March 20.
5. Jim's birthday is March 23.

Page 45, Exercise B

1. b   2. c   3. a

Page 45, Exercise C

1. March 18, 1995
2. August 30, 1978
3. November 29, 1985
4. February 8, 2002

Page 46, Exercise A

1. A: is
   B: He's
2. A: are
   B: is / is
3. A: is
   B: He's
4. A: are
   B: They're
5. A: is
   B: she's

Page 46, Exercise B

José: 14 / ninth grade.
Carmen: 11 / sixth grade.
Miguel: 8 / third grade

Page 47, Exercise D

1. How old is / He's / years old
2. Is he in / he isn't **OR** he's not.
   He's in the fifth grade.
3. How old is / She's / years old
4. Is she in / she is
5. How old is / He's / years old
6. Is he in / he isn't **OR** he's not.
   He's in the ninth grade.

Page 47, Exercise E

Mark: Hi, Nina. Where are you?
Nina: *I'm at my cousin's house*. I'm
      babysitting for her kids.
Mark: Oh, that's nice. *How old are
      they?*

Nina: Well, her daughter is nine.
      *She's in the fourth grade. And
      her son is seven.* He's in the
      second grade.

Page 48, Exercise A

a. 1, 2, 3
b. 1, 2, 3
c. 1, 2, 4
d. 1, 2, 3
e. 1, 2, 4

Page 48, Exercise B

1. Around 50 years old
2. June
3. He's short and heavy. He has
   short hair and a mustache.
   He's a lot of fun.

Page 48, Exercise C

My cousin's name is <u>Lee</u>. She is
15 years old<u>.</u> She is in the tenth
grade. <u>S</u>he's tall and thin. She
is interesting. Her birthday is in
<u>August</u>. She lives in <u>Dallas</u>.

Page 49, Exercise A

Work: Answer a call from your
manager
Home Life: Take care of a sick
child, Talk to your friends on the
phone, Go shopping online

Page 49, Exercise B

1. Daughter: Hi mom.
   Hani: Hi, Nadia. Are you
             OK?
   Daughter: Yes, I'm fine. Where
             / ~~How~~ are you?
   Hani: I'm at work.
   Daughter: Oh, I'm sorry. I
             know you can't
             / ~~can~~ talk on the
             phone at work.
   Hani: That's OK. Can we
             talk at ~~work~~ / home?
   Daughter: OK. Bye!
2. True

Page 49, Exercise C

1. Hani: Can I ask you a
               question?
   Co-worker: I'm sorry. I'm busy.
   Hani: Are you working
               on the report?
   Co-worker: No / ~~Yes~~, I'm
               not. I'm buying
               shoes for my son
               / ~~daughter~~. He's
               eleven.
2. False

Page 49, Exercise D

1. organized
2. money

UNIT 5

Page 50, Exercise A

1. a dress, shoes
2. a sweater, pants, socks
3. a jacket, jeans
4. a T-shirt, pants
5. a shirt, jeans, shoes
6. a blouse, a skirt, shoes

Page 51, Exercise B

1. A black dress and yellow shoes
2. A gray sweater and black pants
3. A blue and white jacket, red
   T-shirt, and black jeans
4. A gray T-shirt and brown pants
5. A pink shirt and blue jeans
6. A white blouse and black skirt

Page 51, Exercise C

1. yellow / It's a yellow shirt.
2. black / They're black socks.
3. pink / It's a pink dress.
4. red / They're red sneakers.
5. purple / It's a purple jacket.
6. khaki / They're khaki pants.

Page 52, Exercise A

1. Jack ~~need~~ / needs a new jacket.
2. Sun-Li ~~want~~ / wants a new
   dress.
3. Sam and Hal need / ~~needs~~ new
   sneakers.

4. I need / ~~needs~~ a new wallet.
5. They want / ~~wants~~ new pants.
6. You need / ~~needs~~ a new jacket.

Page 52, Exercise B

1. Carla has a new watch.
2. Eric has a yellow backpack.
3. I have new shoes.
4. Leo and Mark have new shirts.
5. Matt has a new shirt and jeans.
6. Mr. Lee has black shoes.

Page 52, Exercise C

1. wants
2. needs
3. has
4. want
5. need
6. have
7. needs
8. have
9. want

Page 53, Exercise A

1. 52¢
2. 55¢
3. $1.86
4. $32.14

Page 53, Exercise B

1. A: How much are the jeans?
   B: _They're $39.95._
2. A: How much is the jacket?
   B: _It's $49.00._
3. A: How much _are the pants_?
   B: _They're $69.00._
4. A: How much _is the dress_?
   B: _It's $76.00._
5. A: How much _is the watch_?
   B: _It's $110.00._

Page 53, Exercise C

1. b   2. a   3. b
4. b   5. b   6. b

Page 53, Exercise D

1. Fashion World
2. September 15, 2019

3. $15.99
4. $32.99
5. $25.99

Page 54, Exercise E

74.97 x .095 = _$7.12_
74.97 + _$7.12_ = _$82.09_

Page 54, Exercise F

1. .0950
2. $7.12
3. $82.09
4. .1025
5. $7.68
6. $82.65
7. .07
8. $5.25
9. $80.22

Page 55, Exercise A

1. A: Do
   B: do
2. A: Does
   B: does
3. A: Does
   B: doesn't
4. A: Do
   B: do
5. A: Do
   B: don't
6. A: Do
   B: don't

Page 55, Exercise B

1. Do you have this sweater in a large?
2. Does she want this T-shirt in a medium?
3. Does Tom have a black jacket?
4. Do you like these shoes?
5. Do you have this skirt in blue?
6. Do you have this dress in a medium?

Page 56, Exercise C

1. A: Do / have
   B: do
2. A: Does / need
   B: doesn't / has

3. A: Do / like
   B: do
4. A: Do / need
   B: don't / have
5. A: Does / want
   B: does / likes
6. A: Do / have
   B: don't / have

Page 56, Exercise D

1. Yes, she does.
2. Yes, she does.
3. No, she doesn't.
4. Yes, she does.
5. No, she doesn't.
6. Yes, they do.
7. No, she doesn't.

Page 57, Exercise B

1. a

Page 57, Exercise C

1. Today, more people use a ~~credit card~~ / cash. Line 1
2. One bad thing about a credit card / ~~cash~~ is that there isn't a receipt for everything that you buy. Line 4
3. One bad thing about a credit card / ~~cash~~ is that technology might cause problems with using it. Line 5

Page 58, Exercise A

1. don't
2. doesn't
3. don't
4. doesn't
5. don't
6. doesn't

Page 58, Exercise B

1. don't need
2. don't like
3. doesn't like
4. doesn't fit
5. don't want
6. doesn't need

Page 59, Exercise C

1. He doesn't like the red jacket.
2. She doesn't want the orange sneakers.
3. They don't need new jeans.
4. I don't have my receipt.
5. These pants don't fit.
6. This jacket doesn't fit.
7. She doesn't have a brown backpack.

Page 59, Exercise D

1. The shirt doesn't fit.
2. The watch doesn't work.
3. She doesn't like the jacket.
4. The dress doesn't fit.

Page 60, Exercise A

1. He needs a new jacket, pants, and jeans.
2. Jack wants a new shirt, jeans, and socks for his birthday.
3. She has a new skirt, blouse, and shoes.
4. I wear pants, a white shirt, and black shoes to work.
5. Mia wants a new dress, a skirt, and a blouse for her birthday.

Page 60, Exercise B

My name is Hector. I'm a server at a restaurant. At work, I wear a blue shirt, khaki pants, and brown shoes. At home, I wear a T-shirt, blue jeans, and sneakers.

Page 60, Exercise C

It's my brother's birthday tomorrow. He wants a new shirt, jeans, and a T-shirt. He needs a new jacket, pants, and shoes.

Page 61, Exercise A

a, b, c, d

Page 61, Exercise B

1. Customer: I need / ~~needs~~ to ask you a question.
   Loc: Sure.

Customer: I want / ~~wants~~ this sweater in blue.
Loc: It's a nice sweater.
Customer: Do / ~~Does~~ you have it?
Loc: Yes, we do / ~~don't~~. Let me find a sales assistant to help you.

2. True

Page 61, Exercise C

1. Co-worker: Everyone is using credit cards. It takes a long time!
   Loc: Do you need / ~~needs~~ help?
   Co-worker: No, I ~~do~~ / don't. The customers will have to wait!
   Loc: I can help you, if you ~~wants~~ / want.

2. False

Page 61, Exercise D

1. False   2. True

UNIT 6

Page 62, Exercise A

1. ~~sofa~~
2. ~~closet~~
3. ~~sink~~
4. ~~bed~~
5. ~~shower~~

Page 62, Exercise B

1. microwave
2. refrigerator
3. sink
4. lamp
5. sink
6. bed

Page 63, Exercise C

1. lamp / bedroom
2. dresser / bedroom
3. stove / kitchen
4. chair / dining room
5. table / living room

Page 64, Exercise A

1. *There's* a living room, and *there's* a small kitchen. *There's* no dining room. *There are* two bedrooms, but *there's* no laundry room. *There's* one bathroom. *There's* a garage. *There is* no closet.
2. *There's* a large living room, and *there's* a large kitchen, too. *There's* a small dining room. *There are* two bathrooms and three bedrooms. *There are* two closets, also. *There's* a laundry room, but *there's* no garage.
3. *There's* a living room, but *there's* no dining room. *There's* one bedroom. *There's* one bathroom, but *there are* no closets. *There's* a kitchen, and *there's* a garage.

Page 64, Exercise B

A. 3
B. 2
C. 1

Page 65, Exercise C

1. b   2. a   3. a   4. a

Page 65, Exercise D

2. There's a sofa. There are two lamps. There's no chair and there's no coffee table.

Page 66, Exercise A

1. False   2. True

Page 66, Exercise C

1. Each room in the house should have two ~~windows~~ / exits. Lines 1-2
2. An exit can be a door or a ~~closet~~ / window. Lines 5-6
3. To practice fire safety, first make a map of your ~~windows~~ / home. Line 10
4. Mark the ~~bedrooms~~ / exits on the map. Lines 10-11

5. At the end of the fire drill, everyone should go to the meeting place / ~~kitchen~~. Lines 13-14

Page 67, Exercise A

1. Is there / Yes, there is.
2. Is there / No, there isn't. **OR** No, there's not.
3. Is there / Yes, there is.
4. Is there / Yes, there is.
5. Are there / Yes, there are.
6. Are there / No, there aren't.
7. Is there / No, there isn't. **OR** No, there's not.
8. Is there / Yes, there is.

Page 67, Exercise B

1. A: Is there a one-bedroom apartment for rent?
   B: Yes, there is. There's a furnished apartment for rent.
   A: Are there appliances?
   B: Yes, there are. There are new appliances.
   A: Is there a bed?
   B: Yes, there is. There's a new bed.
   A: Is there a dining room?
   B: No, there's no dining room.
2. A: Is there a two-bedroom apartment for rent?
   B: Yes, there is. There's an unfurnished apartment for rent.
   A: Is there a microwave?
   B: Yes, there is. There's a microwave.
   A: Are there closets?
   B: Yes, there are. There are four closets.
   A: Is there a laundry room?
   B: No, there isn't.

Page 68, Exercise A

1. b   2. a   3. b   4. a   5. a

Page 68, Exercise B

1. St.   3. Ave.   5. Rd.
2. Dr.   4. Blvd.

Page 68, Exercise C

1. c   2. e   3. a   4. b   5. d

Page 69, Exercise E

1. <u>1</u> Bedroom(s) <u>$1,200</u> a month Large <u>kitchen</u> with new <u>stove</u> 14 Bank <u>St.</u>, Apt. <u>3D</u>
2. <u>2</u> Bedroom(s) <u>1</u> Bathroom(s) $1,300 a month Large <u>bathroom</u> with new shower 346 Clover <u>Blvd.</u>, Apt. <u>1C</u>
3. <u>3</u> Bedroom(s) In new <u>building</u> <u>$1,450</u> a month Large <u>dining room</u> 45 Orchard <u>Ave.</u>, Apt. <u>2B</u>
4. <u>1</u> Bedroom(s) <u>$900</u> a month Large <u>living room</u> <u>Laundry room</u> in bldg. 3 Apple <u>Dr.</u>, Apt. 2A

Page 70, Exercise A

1. from   4. to
2. at   5. on
3. in   6. at

Page 70, Exercise B

A: How do I get to Century Manufacturing Company?
B: <u>From</u> here? Let me check on my phone. Okay. Go east <u>on</u> Maple Avenue. Turn left <u>at</u> Bank Street. Then continue <u>on</u> Bank Street to 6th Street. It's <u>on</u> the corner of Bank and 6th.

Page 70, Exercise C

Sam: Hi, Jess. Are you coming <u>to</u> my office?
Jess: Yes, Sam. How do I get there <u>from</u> here? I'm coming <u>from</u> work.
Sam: My office is <u>in</u> Oakdale. First, go <u>to</u> Conner Street. Turn left. Continue north <u>on</u> Conner Street. Then turn left <u>at</u> the light. That's Manor Road. My office is <u>at</u> 58 Manor Road.
Jess: Great!

Page 71, Exercise D

Go (~~south~~ / north) (~~in~~ /on) Powell Street. Continue (~~at~~ / on) Powell Street for three blocks. Turn right (~~on~~/ at) the (~~3rd~~ / 2nd) light. Continue (east / ~~west~~) (~~in~~ / on) Starrett Street. Our store is (~~at~~ / on) Starrett Street (~~in~~ / on) the (~~left~~ / right). It's (at / ~~in~~) 3228 Starrett Street.

Page 71, Exercise E

Ed's Appliances

Page 71, Exercise F

Go <u>south</u> <u>on</u> Powell Street. Continue <u>on</u> Powell Street for one block. Turn left <u>at</u> the light. Continue <u>on</u> Starrett Street for two blocks. Go <u>right</u> on Reed Avenue. Continue <u>on</u> Reed Avenue for two blocks. Turn <u>left</u> on Oak Street. It's <u>at</u> 4118 Oak Street.

Page 72, Exercise A

1. There is a (large) (sunny) room.
2. There are (two) (small) windows.
3. There is a (nice) lamp.
4. There is a (big) (new) microwave.
5. There is a (small) (old) table.

Page 72, Exercise B

My favorite room at home is the living room. It's big and <u>sunny</u>. There is a <u>window</u>. There's a <u>big</u> couch and a <u>small</u> table. There's a <u>lamp</u> next to the <u>table</u>. The best part is the couch.

Page 72, Exercise C

My favorite room at home is the bedroom. It's big and sunny. There <u>are</u> three windows. There's a large closet, and there <u>is</u> a new dresser. There's a large lamp next to a small table.

Page 73, Exercise A

A person who is good at finding information gets / ~~doesn't get~~ answers to important questions.

Page 73, Exercise B

1. Milos: Ms. Hand ~~need~~ / needs a new microwave. Do we have one?
   Building manager: I'm not sure, Milos.
   Milos: I can check downstairs. There are / ~~is~~ many appliance boxes there.
   Building manager: That's a good idea. Thanks, Milos.
2. True

Page 73, Exercise C

1. Renter: Hi. Are you the building manager?
   Milos: No, I'm not / ~~he's not~~. He's not here right now. Can I help you?
   Renter: We want to see the one-bedroom apartment / ~~kitchen~~.
   Milos: I think it's still available. Let me call the manager to see.
2. True

Page 73, Exercise D

1. False   2. True

UNIT 7

Page 74, Exercise A

1. the dishes
2. breakfast
3. to work
4. a shower
5. dressed
6. homework

Page 74, Exercise B

1. gets home
2. exercises
3. cooks dinner
4. eats dinner
5. washes the dishes / watches TV
6. reads
7. takes a shower
8. goes to bed

Page 75, Exercise C

1. A: get up
   B: 5:00
2. A: take a shower
   B: 5:15
3. A: get dressed
   B: 5:30
4. A: eat breakfast
   B: 5:45
5. A: go to work
   B: 6:00

Page 76, Exercise A

1. do / work
2. does / get up
3. do / have
4. do / go
5. does / start
6. does / get

Page 76, Exercise B

1. A: What time do you get home?
   B: At 6:30.
2. A: What time do they go to work?
   B: At 7:15.
3. A: What time does Arnold exercise?
   B: At 12:00.
4. A: What time does she eat breakfast?
   B: At 6:00.
5. A: What time do Jason and Marie eat dinner?
   B: At 5:30.

Page 77, Exercise C

1. From / to / on
2. On
3. From / to
4. At
5. At / on

Page 77, Exercise D

1. He works on Sundays from 12:00-5:00.
2. He has English class on Wednesdays from 7:00-9:00.
3. He plays soccer on Thursdays from 4:00-7:00.
4. He babysits on Fridays from 3:00-6:00.
5. He has a computer class on Saturdays from 1:00-3:00.

Page 78, Exercise A

Wednesday: 1:00-5:00 English class
Thursday: 10:00-2:00 work
Friday: lunch

Page 78, Exercise B

1. 7:00 P.M. / 12:00 A.M. / Tuesday / Thursday
2. Monday(s) / Wednesday(s) / Friday(s)
3. 9:00 A.M.
4. 1:00 P.M.
5. 6:00 A.M. / 12:00 P.M.
6. 20

Page 79, Exercise C

1. Tuesdays / Thursdays / Saturdays
2. 11:00 A.M.
3. 11:00 A.M. / 7:00 P.M.
4. 8:00 A.M.
5. Saturdays

Page 80, Exercise A

1. never
2. always
3. never
4. always
5. always
6. sometimes

Page 80, Exercise B

1. Sarah usually shops for food on Saturdays.
2. Martin always takes a shower at night.
3. Conor sometimes rides his bike on Sundays.
4. They never do laundry on Sundays.

Page 81, Exercise C

1. He usually goes to the park.
2. She sometimes plays basketball.
3. He always shops for food.
4. He never goes dancing.
5. She sometimes cleans. **OR** She sometimes cleans the house.
6. She always goes swimming.

Page 82, Exercise D

1. b. Line 1
2. c. Lines 2-3
3. a **OR** b **OR** c. Lines 4-9

Page 82, Exercise E

1. b. Line 1
2. c. Lines 2-3
3. b **OR** c. Lines 6-7 **OR** Line 9

Page 83, Exercise A

1. does / listen to music
2. do / go running
3. do / play video games
4. does / ride her bike
5. does / work
6. do / have English class

Page 83, Exercise B

Go running: Three times a week
Take a long walk: Once a week
Do puzzles: Every day
Listen to music: Never

Page 84, Exercise A

1. (M)onday is my favorite day. I don't work on (M)ondays.
2. Charlie works on (T)uesdays, (T)hursdays, and (F)ridays.
3. Jim often relaxes at home on (F)ridays.
4. Mandy usually works on (S)aturdays and (S)undays.
5. I never work on (F)riday.

Page 84, Exercise B

1. Mondays
2. Tuesday(s), Wednesday(s), Thursday (s)
3. Saturday(s)
4. Sunday(s)
5. Friday(s)

Page 84, Exercise C

My favorite day of the week is Ṣaturday. I never work on Saturday. I stay home and spend time with family. I usually play basketball with my brother ~~on~~ in the morning. I sometimes meet friends for lunch. I usually go to the movies ~~in~~ at night. I love Ṣaturday. It's the best day of the week.

Page 85, Exercise A

1. a

Page 85, Exercise B

1. Rita: Are you leaving?
   Co-worker: Yes. It's time for me to go.
   Rita: When ~~does~~ / do you finish work?
   Co-worker: I work from / ~~on~~ 9 to / ~~from~~ 5. It's 5 o'clock.
   Rita: But the manager needs / ~~need~~ these reports today.
   Co-worker: Well, I have plans.
2. False

Page 85, Exercise C

1. Co-worker: I can't do this. I ~~always~~ / never do it right.
   Rita: What's wrong?
   Co-worker: My timesheet isn't / ~~aren't~~ correct.
   Rita: I can help you. Always / ~~Sometimes~~ put the days of the week here.
   Co-worker: Oh, I see. I ~~usual~~ / usually make that mistake. Thank you, Rita.
   Rita: You're welcome. I'm happy to help.
2. True

Page 85, Exercise D

1. True
2. False

UNIT 8

Page 86, Exercise A

1. yogurt
2. cereal
3. oranges
4. apples
5. bananas
6. eggs
7. bread
8. butter

Page 86, Exercise B

1. cabbage
2. onions
3. chicken
4. potatoes
5. rice
6. beans
7. milk
8. beef
9. lettuce
10. cheese

Page 87, Exercise C

1. grains
2. vegetables
3. fruit
4. protein
5. dairy

Page 88, Exercise A

Count	Non-count
apple	beef
egg	butter
pancake	cereal
potato	lettuce
taco	pasta
wrap	yogurt

Page 88, Exercise B

1. bananas / them
2. steak / it
3. yogurt / it
4. cereal / it
5. potatoes / them
6. eggs / them

Page 89, Exercise C

1. pancakes   4. cabbage
2. apples   5. fish
3. oranges   6. pasta

Page 89, Exercise D

A: a hamburger
A: a taco / tacos
B: a taco
A: pizza
B: Pizza / pizza
A: pizza

Page 90, Exercise A

1. a   2. b

Page 90, Exercise C

1. c. Line 5
2. b. Line 9
3. a. Lines 14-15
4. b. Line 16

Page 91, Exercise A

1. c   3. b   5. a
2. f   4. e   6. d

Page 91, Exercise B

a green salad
a hamburger
large fries
a large soda
a bowl of soup
a chicken sandwich
a baked potato
a large iced tea
apple pie

Page 92, Exercise A

1. $4.29 a pound
2. 99¢ a pound
3. $4.29
4. $3.29 a pound
5. $6.99 a pound
6. 79¢ a pound
7. 89¢

Page 92, Exercise B

Quick-Shop: Chicken, Bread, Steak, Apples

All-Natural: Potatoes, Cheese, Yogurt

Page 93, Exercise C

1. b   3. b   5. a
2. a   4. b

Page 93, Exercise D

1. 10
2. 9
3. 120
4. 110
5. 150 milligrams
6. 220 milligrams
7. 12 grams
8. 24 grams
9. Cereal B

Page 94, Exercise A

1. A: How much butter
   B: Not much
2. A: How many onions
   B: Not many
3. A: How much ice cream
   B: A lot
4. A: How much milk
   B: Not much
5. A: How much yogurt
   B: A lot
6. A: How much cereal
   B: A lot
7. A: How many tomatoes
   B: Not many
8. A: How many peppers
   B: A lot

Page 95, Exercise B

1. A: much turkey
   B: two pounds
2. A: much rice
   B: twelve ounces
3. A: many peppers
   B: two
4. A: many onions
   B: three
5. A: much milk
   B: eight ounces
6. A: much cheese
   B: ten ounces
7. A: much vegetable oil
   B: two ounces

Page 95, Exercise C

Check (✓) the following foods:
apple pie; green salad; grilled chicken; juice; rice; soda; water

Page 96, Exercise A

1. I have tacos for lunch.
2. He has juice every day.
3. I drink a cup of coffee every morning.
4. She has vegetables five times a week.
5. Ana eats eggs for breakfast every day.

Page 96, Exercise B

Every morning Carl drinks coffee. He usually has **OR** eats cereal for breakfast. For lunch, Carl usually eats **OR** has a turkey sandwich and a salad. Carl sometimes has **OR** eats fish for dinner. Once a week he goes to a restaurant for dinner. He usually eats **OR** has a hamburger and fries.

Page 96, Exercise C

In the morning, I usually ~~has~~ _have_ three eggs, cereal, and juice. For lunch, I usually eat tacos and pizza. I usually ~~eat~~ _have_ **OR** _drink_ a large soda. For dinner, I eat chicken and rice. At night sometimes I ~~take~~ _eat_ **OR** _have_ ice cream. That's a lot of food!

Page 97, Exercise A

A person who takes action makes / ~~doesn't make~~ decisions on his or her own.

Page 97, Exercise B

1. Server: It's so busy! We don't have / ~~has~~ any clean ~~glass~~ / glasses.
   Nasir: Oh, I see. These tables aren't clean. There is still ~~a rice~~ / rice on them.
   Server: Yes, I know. The other server is new. There are many / ~~much~~ glasses on the dirty tables.
   Nasir: Let me help you. We can bring the glasses into the kitchen. I'll wash them quickly.
2. True

Page 97, Exercise C

1. Cook: Oh, no. The tomatoes / ~~tomatos~~ are bad! I can't use them.
   Nasir: Can I help? I could go to the farmer's market. How many / ~~much~~ tomatoes do you need?
   Cook: We'll need about 20 pounds.
   Nasir: That's no problem. Do you need any potatoes ~~and~~ / or onions?
   Cook: No, I have enough.
2. False

Page 97, Exercise D

1. True   2. False

UNIT 9

Page 98, Exercise A

hot: 95–110
warm: 70–85
cool: 45–60
cold: 20–35

Page 98, Exercise B

1. c   2. b   3. a   4. d

Page 98, Exercise C

1. It's warm and cloudy.
2. It's cool and rainy.
3. It's hot and sunny.
4. It's cold and snowy.

Page 99, Exercise A

1. is not working
2. are visiting
3. is not sleeping
4. is studying
5. are not eating
6. are making

Page 99, Exercise B

1. She's talking on the phone.
2. We're watching TV.
3. I'm reading a book.
4. It's raining in Chicago.
5. He's riding his bike.
6. They're running in the park.
7. She's wearing a new jacket.
8. We're visiting our friends in Miami.

Page 100, Exercise C

1. 's talking
2. isn't drinking OR 's not drinking
3. isn't eating OR 's not eating
4. isn't doing OR 's not doing
5. 's listening
6. 's doing
7. 's drinking
8. isn't talking OR 's not talking
9. 're sitting
10. aren't watching TV OR 're not watching TV

Page 100, Exercise D

1. He's cleaning the floor.
2. She's listening to music.
3. She's sleeping.
4. He's reading.
5. She's cooking.

Page 101, Exercise A

1. d   3. c   5. f
2. b   4. a   6. e

Page 102, Exercise C

1. You are in the office marked "X." During the drill, go to the exit / ~~entrance~~.
2. Do not use the elevators / ~~stairways~~.
3. Exit the building / ~~elevator~~ quickly.
4. Go outside. Wait in the parking lot / ~~office~~.

Page 102, Exercise D

1. water
2. cash OR money
3. cellphone OR car

Page 103, Exercise A

1. a. No, she isn't. OR No, she's not.
   b. No, she isn't. OR No, she's not.
   c. Yes, she is.
2. a. No, he isn't. OR No, he's not.
   b. Yes, he is.
   c. Yes, he is.
3. a. Yes, they are.
   b. No, they aren't. OR No, they're not.
   c. No, it isn't. OR No, it's not.

Page 104, Exercise B

1. A: Is / studying English
   B: she isn't OR she's not
2. A: Are / listening to music?
   B: I'm not
3. A: Are / shopping for food
   B: I'm not
4. A: Is / raining
   B: it is
5. A: Are / going home
   B: they aren't OR they're not
6. A: Is / snowing
   B: it isn't OR it's not

Page 104, Exercise C

Ann: Are you watching the news?
Tim: *No, I'm not. I'm reading a*
magazine.
Ann: Well, turn on the TV. A big storm is coming.
Tim: *Really?*
Ann: Yes. In fact, I'm coming home early. I'm at the grocery store now.
Tim: *Oh, good. Are you getting*
water?
Ann: Yes. I'm getting water, food, and a lot of batteries.
Tim: *Great. Get matches, too.*
Ann: OK. Do we need anything else?
Tim: *Yes. We need good weather!*

Page 105, Exercise B

1. c   2. c

Page 105, Exercise C

1. b. Lines 1-2
2. c. Lines 2-3
3. c. Line 6

Page 105, Exercise D

1. b   2. c

Page 106, Exercise A

1. earmuffs / gloves
2. sunblock
3. a raincoat / an umbrella
4. sunglasses
5. a scarf / boots

Page 106, Exercise B

1. It's really hot and humid in Dallas today.
2. It's pretty cold and snowing in Boston now. **OR** It's snowing and pretty cold in Boston now.
3. It's very foggy in San Francisco in the winter.
4. The weather in New York is pretty nice in the spring.

Page 107, Exercise C

1. b   2. a   3. b   4. a   5. b

Page 108, Exercise A

1. it's warm, but not hot
2. I love the cold weather
3. it's very cold
4. I work outside
5. I like to swim

Page 108, Exercise B

1. I love Boston because the winter there is beautiful.
2. Winter is my favorite season because I like the snow.
3. I always wear gloves in the winter because my hands get very cold.

Page 108, Exercise C

I love San Francisco. It's my favorite city because I ~~don't~~ love the weather there. In the summer, *it's* warm. It's not very hot. Fall is my favorite season because it is usually warm and sunny. In the winter, it is sometimes rainy. In the spring, it *is* very cool.

Page 109, Exercise A

a, b, d, e

Page 109, Exercise B

1. Co-worker: We have a new app for taking attendance. I am / ~~are~~ using it. It's great!
   Yefim: Is it / ~~It is~~ easy to use?
   Co-worker: Yes, it's really / ~~never~~ easy. I can show you.
   Yefim: That's pretty / ~~nice~~ good! You know I don't like new technology.

Co-worker: It's not very difficult.
Yefim: That sounds good. I ~~is~~ / am going to try it.

2. True

Page 109, Exercise C

1. Co-worker: We're having / ~~have~~ another meeting about the new computers.
   Yefim: That's a very / ~~vary~~ good idea, isn't it?
   Co-worker: I don't think so.
   Yefim: Why not?
   Co-worker: I really / ~~real~~ don't want to go. I know how to use a computer. We don't need / ~~needing~~ more meetings.
   Yefim: Well, you might learn something new at the meeting.

2. True

Page 109, Exercise D

1. True   2. False

UNIT 10

Page 110, Exercise A

1. a supermarket
2. a clothing store
3. an ATM
4. a bank
5. a park
6. a drugstore
7. a laundromat
8. a café
9. a gas station
10. a fire station
11. a post office
12. a bus stop
13. a police station
14. a salon

Page 111, Exercise B

1. on Seaview Boulevard
2. on Oyster Road
3. on Seaview Boulevard
4. on Oyster Road
5. on Erie Street
6. on Oyster Road
7. on Seaview Boulevard
8. on Seaview Boulevard OR on Erie Street

Page 111, Exercise C

1. c 3. a 5. d
2. e 4. f 6. b

Page 112, Exercise A

1. The post office is on / ~~near~~ Central Drive between / ~~next to~~ Chestnut Avenue and Cedar Lane.
2. The courthouse is on / ~~near~~ Mill Road ~~between~~ / next to the DMV.
3. The bank is across ~~from~~ / next to the café.
4. The gym is across from / ~~next to~~ Hink's Clothing Store.
5. The gas station is on the corner of / ~~near~~ Cedar Lane and Brook Avenue.
6. The supermarket is down / ~~on~~ the block from the laundromat.
7. The police station is ~~across from~~ / next to the fire station.
8. The drugstore is around the corner / ~~across from~~ the hotel.

Page 113, Exercise B

1. on the corner of
2. near
3. between
4. down the block
5. near
6. on the corner of
7. around the corner
8. down the block
9. around the corner
10. between

Page 113, Exercise C

1. the café
2. the gym
3. the supermarket

Page 114, Exercise A

1. I drive.
2. She rides her bike.
3. They take the subway.
4. She takes the bus.
5. He takes a taxi.
6. They take the train.

Page 114, Exercise B

1. 8:40
2. Maple Avenue
3. 8:52
4. 8:44
5. 4th Avenue
6. 8:53
7. 9:06
8. South Drive
9. Elm Street
10. 9:08

Page 115, Exercise A

Meg: *How do you get to the high school?*
Rob: Take the Number 12 train.
Meg: Ok. *Where do you get the train?*
Rob: Around the corner on Colombo Road.
Meg: Great. *Where do you buy a ticket?*
Rob: In the station.
Meg: Thanks. One more question. *How much does the train cost?*
Rob: $2.50.

Page 115, Exercise C

Mark: *Which bus goes to the high school?*
Lisa: The Number 27 bus goes to the high school.
Mark: OK. *What time does the bus leave the station?*

Lisa: At 7:15.
Mark: *How much does the bus cost?*
Lisa: $3.50.
Mark: Thanks. One more question. *Where do you get off?*
Lisa: Dupont Square.

Page 116, Exercise E

A: *How do* you get to Watertown High School?
B: Take the Number 8 bus.
A: *Where do* you get it?
B: At Crawford Street.
A: *How much does* it cost?
B: $3.50.
A: *Where do* you get off?
B: At Newport Avenue.

Page 116, Exercise F

1. How do you get to Nick's Café?
2. How much does the train cost?
3. Where do you get off?
4. Where do you get the Number 6 bus?
5. How much does the bus cost?
6. How do you get to the library?
7. Where do you buy a ticket for the bus?
8. How do you get to the train station?

Page 117, Exercise B

Answers will vary.
Possible answer: You can mail letters and packages.

Page 117, Exercise C

1. a. Line 2
2. c. Lines 4-5
3. a. Line 5
4. c. Lines 11-12

Page 118, Exercise A

A: are / doing
B: 'm going
A: are / going

B: 's going
A: are / getting
B: 're driving

Page 118, Exercise B

1. A: is
   B: He's going to a concert
2. A: are
   B: I'm playing basketball
3. A: are
   B: They're going to the mall. OR
      They're going shopping.
4. A: 's
   B: She's riding her bike.
5. A: 's
   B: He's studying.

Page 119, Exercise C

1. Where is he going this
   weekend?
2. What are you doing on
   Saturday night?
3. Who are you going with to
   the movies?
4. How is your sister getting to
   the concert?
5. Who are you playing soccer
   with on Sunday?
6. What are they doing on Friday
   night?

Page 119, Exercise D

Saturday, 9:50,
Sunday, 3:00
Saturday, 8:00

Page 120, Exercise A

1. I live on Broadway.
2. The café is next to the library.
3. The bus stop is down the
   block.
4. The supermarket is around the
   corner from my house.
5. The drugstore is between the
   police station and the salon.

Page 120, Exercise B

My street
I live at 28 Maple Street. I take
the bus to work. The bus stop is

down the block. There's a café on
Lakeview Road. Next to the café
is a gym. The library is around
the corner from the café. I like my
street because everything is close
by.

Page 120, Exercise C

I live in on Elm Street. There are a
lot of stores near my home. There
is a supermarket on down the
block from my house. There's a
café in on the corner and a salon
across the street. And a drugstore
is around down the street from my
house.

Page 121, Exercise A

a, c, e

Page 121, Exercise B

1. Nurse: Ani, I have an
          emergency between /
          down the hall. I have to
          leave.
   Ani: How / What can I help?
   Nurse: When do you start / you
          start your shift?
   Ani: I'm start / starting at
          4:00.
   Nurse: Can you help with Mrs.
          King? I'm giving / give
          her breakfast.
   Ani: Of course.
   Nurse: Thank you, Ani.
2. True

Page 121, Exercise C

1. Ani: Carla. The
               supervisor is
               looking / look for
               you.
   Co-worker: Sorry I'm late. The
               traffic was really /
               not bad.
   Ani: Where/ How much
               was it bad?
   Co-worker: It was bad
               between / over
               George Street and
               Purple Lane.

Ani: I'm going / go to
           let the supervisor
           know you're here.
           You should call.
Co-worker: Oh, well. I don't
           think it's important
           to call.

2. False

Page 121, Exercise D

1. True   2. False

UNIT 11

Page 122, Exercise A

1.	head	11.	shoulder
2.	face	12.	stomach
3.	eye	13.	leg
4.	teeth	14.	foot
5.	mouth	15.	wrist
6.	ear	16.	arm
7.	nose	17.	neck
8.	hand	18.	back
9.	elbow	19.	knee
10.	chest	20.	ankle

Page 123, Exercise B

Parts of the head: ears, eyes,
mouth, nose
Parts of the arm: elbow, hand,
wrist
Parts of the leg: ankle, foot, knee

Page 123, Exercise C

1. feet
2. leg
3. head
4. hands
5. shoulders
6. arms

Page 124, Exercise A

A: do / feel
B: feel
A: Do / have
B: don't have / hurts

Page 124, Exercise B

1. the flu
2. a headache

3. a stomachache
4. an earache

Page 125, Exercise C

1. has / doesn't have
2. don't feel / have
3. has / hurts
4. doesn't feel / hurts
5. feels / has
6. don't feel / have

Page 125, Exercise D

A: How does Ericka feel?
B: Her head hurts.
A: Does she have a fever?
B: No, she doesn't have a fever.
A: Does she have a stuffy nose?
B: Yes, she has a stuffy nose.

Page 126, Exercise A

14 / 10:30

Page 126, Exercise B

Assistant: Children's Clinic. Can I help you?
Mrs. Pietro: This is Mrs. Pietro. I'd like to make an appointment for my son.
Assistant: Sure. What is your son's name?
Mrs. Pietro: His name is _Alex_.
Assistant: Can he come in on Thursday?
Mrs. Pietro: No, I'm sorry.
Assistant: How about _Friday_?
Mrs. Pietro: Yes, that's good.
Assistant: Is _4:30_ OK?
Mrs. Pietro: Yes, we can be there.
Assistant: OK, that's _Friday, January 31_ at _4:30_ P.M. See you then.

Page 127, Exercise C

1. step
2. sit
3. roll up
4. Open / say
5. take
6. lie down

Page 127, Exercise D

1. 6 hours / 2 tablets / No, he can't.
2. 4 hours / 1 tablet / Yes, she can.

Page 128, Exercise A

1. was / wasn't
2. wasn't / was
3. wasn't /was
4. were / weren't
5. weren't / were

Page 128, Exercise B

1. Hung / was
2. Dominik / Ria / weren't
3. Yoko OR Hung
4. Carolina / wasn't
5. Carolina OR Rita OR Dominik

Page 128, Exercise C

I _was_ in New York last night. I _was_ at a party. It _was_ a surprise party for my parents. The problem _was_ that my parents _weren't_ there. They _were_ both at home. My parents _were_ both sick. The surprise was on us! It _wasn't_ much fun without my parents.

Page 129, Exercise B

1. Yes   2. Yes

Page 129, Exercise C

1. c. Line 2
2. c. Line 1
3. b. Line 6
4. b. Lines 6-7

Page 130, Exercise A

1. should
2. shouldn't
3. should
4. shouldn't
5. should
6. shouldn't

Page 130, Exercise B

Sara: Hi, Joe. This is Sara.

Joe: Hi, Sara. _How are you? Is something wrong?_
Sara: Well, I'm sick. I'm not coming to work today.
Joe: _Oh, I'm sorry to hear that. What do you have?_
Sara: I'm not sure. I have a headache, and my stomach doesn't feel good.
Joe: _Do you have a fever?_
Sara: Yes, I do. I just feel terrible.
Joe: Well, take it easy, Sara. _You should rest and drink a lot._
Sara: That's a good idea.
Joe: But call the doctor if you don't feel better soon. _You really shouldn't wait too long._
Sara: OK. Thanks Joe.

Page 131, Exercise D

1. should use a heating pad
2. should take a hot shower
3. shouldn't take antibiotics
4. should eat a piece of onion
5. shouldn't put butter on it
6. shouldn't drink milk or juice

Page 132, Exercise A

1, 3

Page 132, Exercise B

My mother has good habits for her health.

Page 132, Exercise C

I have healthy and unhealthy habits. I love to eat fruit. I don't ~~likes~~ _like_ vegetables that much. I always eat a good breakfast. I don't eat a healthy lunch. I sometimes just ~~has~~ _have_ a soda. I go to the doctor for a check-up once a year. I ~~gets~~ _get_ exercise 2 times a week. I should exercise 4 or 5 times a week. I get 7 hours of sleep a night. I should _get_ 8 hours.

Page 133, Exercise A

a, c

Page 133, Exercise B

1. Supervisor: Aya, why didn't you finish the report?
   Aya: I'm sorry, Ms. Smith. I'm not feeling / ~~feel~~ well.
   Supervisor: Okay, Aya. I'm sorry that you're not feeling well. How / ~~What~~ do you feel now?
   Aya: I was / ~~were~~ very sick yesterday. I still feel sick today.
   Supervisor: You can bring / ~~brings~~ your laptop home. You can work when you're feeling better.
   Aya: Thank you. I'll have the report tomorrow.
2. True

Page 133, Exercise C

1. Aya: What's wrong, Sam. You don't look well.
   Co-worker: My head ~~hurt~~ / hurts this morning.
   Aya: Are you better now?
   Co-worker: I took some medicine for the headache, but now I feel / ~~feels~~ very sleepy.
   Aya: You should / ~~shouldn't~~ tell the supervisor. You should probably go / ~~goes~~ home.
   Co-worker: I guess you're right. I'm not doing / ~~do~~ very good work right now.
2. False

Page 133, Exercise D

1. True   2. True

UNIT 12

Page 134, Exercise A

1. answers the phone
2. drives a truck
3. takes care of grounds
4. helps customers
5. makes food
6. uses a cash register

Page 135, Exercise B

1. She's taking care of children.
2. He's fixing things.
3. She's making copies.
4. He's supervising workers.
5. He's working on a building.
6. He's using a computer.

Page 135, Exercise C

1. ~~a computer~~
2. ~~a message~~
3. ~~boxes~~
4. ~~children~~
5. ~~homework~~

Page 136, Exercise A

1. can organize
2. can use
3. can take
4. can write
5. can work
6. can make
7. can help
8. can speak

Page 136, Exercise B

1. can't
2. can
3. can't
4. can't
5. can
6. can
7. can
8. can't

Page 137, Exercise C

1. He can drive a truck.
2. She can't use a cash register.
3. He can work on buildings.
4. She can't help customers.
5. He can take care of grounds.
6. He can't fix things. OR He can't fix sinks.

Page 138, Exercise A

A

Page 138, Exercise B

1. Job A is a part-time / ~~full-time~~ job.
2. Job B pays ~~$9~~ / $12 an hour.
3. Job C is a ~~part-time~~ / full-time job.
4. ~~Job A~~ / Job B is 12 hours a week.
5. You need experience for Job A / ~~Job C~~.
6. You can call Devon about ~~Job B~~ / Job C.

Page 138, Exercise C

1. B   2. C   3. A

Page 139, Exercise D

1. Job B
2. $420
3. Job B
4. Job C
5. Job A
6. Job A
7. $180

Page 140, Exercise A

1. A: _Can he_ fix computers?
   B: _No, he can't._
2. A: _Can she_ drive a truck?
   B: _Yes, she can._
3. A: _Can they_ cook?
   B: _Yes, they can._
4. A: _Can she_ make furniture?
   B: _Yes, she can._
5. A: _Can he_ use a cash register?
   B: _No, he can't._
6. A: _Can they_ lift a stove?
   B: _No, they can't._

Page 141, Exercise B

1. A: Can you work on Saturdays?
   B: No, I can't.
2. A: Can you work on Sundays?
   B: Yes, I can.
3. A: Can you work on Monday nights?
   B: Yes, I can.
4. A: Can you work on Tuesday nights?
   B: No, I can't.
5. A: Can you work on Friday nights?
   B: No, I can't.
6. A: Can you work on Wednesday mornings?
   B: No, I can't.

Page 141, Exercise C

A: I'm here about a job. I noticed the Help Wanted sign.
B: *OK. Which job?*
A: The cashier's job. I can use a cash register.
B: *Can you use a computer?*
A: No, I can't, but I can learn.
B: *Can you answer the phone?*
A: Sure. I can answer the phone.
B: *Can you start now?*
A: Yes, I can.
B: Great! You can have the job! Welcome to Yao's Chinese Restaurant.

Page 142, Exercise B

b

Page 142, Exercise C

1. b. Lines 2-3
2. a. Lines 4-5
3. b. Line 7
4. a. Lines 9-10
5. b. Lines 11-12

Page 143, Exercise A

1. Were / was
2. Was / wasn't
3. Were / weren't
4. Were / weren't
5. Was / was
6. were
7. was
8. were
9. was / was
10. was / was

Page 143, Exercise B

1. Were your parents in Colombia last year?
2. How long was she a caregiver?
3. What store was her job at?
4. Was Ms. Roberts sick last week?
5. Were you a nurse in that hospital?
6. Was his job full-time?

Page 144, Exercise A

1. (Mr. King) can make furniture.
2. (She) can't write reports.
3. (I) can work with numbers.
4. (My) last job was at a restaurant.
5. (His) job interview was last Wednesday.

Page 144, Exercise B

I have a job interview tomorrow. I have a lot of experience. I work in an office now. I can use *a computer*. I can make *copies*. I can also answer *phones*. I want to learn more about computers. I want to start my own online company selling photos.

Page 144, Exercise C

I want a job in technology. I can *repair* OR *fix* OR *use* computers. I can also *fix* OR *repair* cell phones. I have experience in technology. I was a repair person at an electronics store. I *was* there for two years. Now I work in an office. I can't *write* well in English, but I can learn.

Page 145, Exercise A

If a person responds well to feedback, he or she learns from / doesn't change after it.

Page 145, Exercise B

1. Kai: Good morning, Ms. Smith.
   Supervisor: Good morning, Kai. You did good / bad work today. I know that you're new. Are you enjoying the job?
   Kai: Yes / No. I love it!
   Supervisor: I can / can't understand that you have a lot to learn.
   Kai: I'm trying / try to do my best.
   Supervisor: Well, keep doing well!
2. True

Page 145, Exercise C

1. Supervisor: Excuse me, Kai. Were / Where you on a break?
   Kai: Yes, I was / were.
   Supervisor: Can you please tell me when you take a break? You should tell / telling someone.
   Kai: Oh, I'm sorry Ms. Smith. Yes, I can / can't do that.
   Supervisor: Thank you.
   Kai: I will tell a co-worker / my friend next time.
2. False

Page 145, Exercise D

1. True   2. False